A COLLECTION OF PROBLEMS IN
ATOMIC AND NUCLEAR PHYSICS

I. YE. IRODOV

A Collection of Problems
in Atomic and
Nuclear Physics

TRANSLATED BY

STEVAN DEDIJER

EDITED BY

S. DONIACH

PERGAMON PRESS

OXFORD · LONDON · EDINBURGH · NEW YORK
PARIS · FRANKFURT

Pergamon Press Ltd., Headington Hill Hall, Oxford
4 & 5 Fitzroy Square, London W. 1

Pergamon Press (Scotland) Ltd., 2 & 3 Teviot Place, Edinburgh 1

Pergamon Press Inc., 44–01 21st Street, Long Island City, New York 11101

Pergamon Press S.A.R.L., 24 rue des Écoles, Paris 5ᵉ

Pergamon Press GmbH, Kaiserstrasse 75, Frankfurt-am-Main

First English edition 1966

Library of Congress Catalog Card No. 64-25444

This translation has been made from the second edition of
I. Ye. Irodov's book entitled
Sbornik zadach po atomnoi fizike,
published in Moscow by Gosatomizdat.

MADE IN GREAT BRITAIN

1787/66

CONTENTS

v

95055

NOTE ABOUT REFERENCES

Many textbooks in English are available at the present time which cover the material of this book. However, a comprehensive students' textbook often does not go into great detail about points which may arise in connection with these problems. Reference has therefore been made in specific cases to more specialized text-books, which should be sufficiently well established to be found in a library covering this subject. The numbers in brackets above the text in all cases refer to references listed at the end of the *questions section* of the same chapter.

S. DONIACH

PREFACE TO THE SECOND EDITION

THIS is the second edition of *A Collection of Problems in Atomic Physics*, published by the Atom Publishing House in 1959. The purpose of this edition of the book is the same as of the first one: to serve as a teaching aid in a general atomic and nuclear physics course.

The book contains approximately 850 problems with sufficiently detailed hints for the solution of the more complicated of them. To facilitate the students' task each chapter is preceded by a brief outline of the fundamental concepts and expressions needed for the solution of the problems contained therein. A summary of the basic physical constants and a series of tables is given at the end of the book.

In the second edition the book has been considerably changed and expanded.

Although on the whole the general arrangement of material of the first edition has been kept, the following changes have been made:

1. Three new chapters have been added: "The Schrödinger equation", "Properties of the Atomic Nucleus" and "Elementary Particles".

2. Almost all chapters have been considerably changed. In many places the sequence of problems has been altered for pedagogical reasons.

3. New tables have been added in the Appendix. As a result certain necessary data have been left out from a number of problems. This was done to help the students to acquire the habit of consulting reference literature.

4. To render the use of the book easier almost all chapters have been divided into sections, each with its appropriate heading.

5. The total number of problems has been increased by more than a half and the number of figures has been trebled.

In conclusion, the author considers it a pleasure to thank all those colleagues who have pointed out errors and misprints in the first edition. The author is especially obliged to docent Ch. K. Muhtarov, who has carefully checked the manuscript of this edition and made a series of valuable suggestions.

I. IRODOV

Problems

1. THERMAL RADIATION

1. The radiative power $d\Phi$ of electromagnetic radiation from an area $\Delta\sigma$ within a solid angle $d\omega$ whose axis forms an angle ϑ with the normal to the area, is

$$d\Phi = J\Delta\sigma\cos\vartheta\,d\omega,$$

where J is the black body radiation intensity.

2. From the fact that radiation in thermal equilibrium is isotropic we have the following relations.

$$I = \pi J,$$

$$\varrho = \frac{4}{c}I,$$

where I is the total emissive power, J the black body radiation intensity, ϱ the energy density of radiation, c the velocity of light.

Similar relations also hold between the corresponding spectral distribution functions I_ν, J_ν and ϱ_ν, defined per unit frequency in terral.

3. *Kirchhoff's law*: the ratio between the emissive power E_ν of a body and its absorptive power A_ν at a given temperature is a function of frequency and absolute temperature only:

$$\frac{E_\nu}{A_\nu} = I(\nu, T).$$

4. *Wien's law* giving the spectral distribution of the energy density as a function of frequency for black body radiation is:

$$\varrho_\nu = \nu^3 f\left(\frac{\nu}{T}\right).$$

5. *Wien's displacement law* states that

$$\lambda_{\max} T = \text{const},$$

where $\lambda_{\max}$ is the wavelength at the maximum of the energy distribution function ϱ_λ in the black body radiation spectrum; the value of Wien's constant is 0·29 cm . deg.

3

6. *The Stefan–Boltzmann law* states that

$$I = \sigma T^4,$$

where I is the total emissive power, σ the Stefan–Boltzmann constant ($\sigma = 5 \cdot 7 \times 10^{-5}$ erg/cm^2 . sec . deg^4), T the absolute temperature of the radiation.

7. The relation between the pressure p and the energy density ϱ of isotropic black body radiation is given by

$$p = \frac{1}{4} \varrho.$$

8. The fundamental energy equation of thermodynamics is:

$$T\,\mathrm{d}S = \mathrm{d}U + \delta A,$$

where T is the absolute temperature, $\mathrm{d}S$ the entropy increment, $\mathrm{d}U$ the intrinsic energy increment, δA the work done by the body (through radiation) in a quasi-static (equilibrium) process.

9. *Planck's radiation law* for the spectral distribution of the energy density of black body radiation states that

$$\varrho(v, T) = \frac{8\pi h v^3}{c^3} \frac{1}{e^{hv/kT} - 1},$$

where v is the radiation frequency, h Planck's constant, ($6 \cdot 62 \times 10^{-27}$ erg . sec), c the velocity of light in vacuum.

10. The average value of a quantity $A(\alpha)$ is defined by:

$$\bar{A} = \frac{\int A(\alpha) f(\alpha)\,\mathrm{d}\alpha}{\int f(\alpha)\,\mathrm{d}\alpha},$$

where $f(\alpha)$ is the distribution function of α.

THERMODYNAMICS OF RADIATION

1.1. Give the dimensions, in the c.g.s. system of units, of the following physical quantities:

(a) the energy density ϱ, the radiation intensity J and the emissive power I;

(b) The spectral distribution of energy density ϱ_v and the spectral radiation intensity J_v.

1.2. Calculate the total energy of isotropic electromagnetic radiation which crosses a small area $\Delta\sigma = 1$ cm^2 in one direction in a time $\tau = 1$ min, if the radiation intensity is $J = 10^5$ erg/cm^2 . sec.

1.3. What is the basic difference between black body radiation and such other kinds of radiation as chemiluminescence, photoluminescence, electroluminescence, and cathodeluminescence?

1.4. A piece of steel, heated to about 800°C, glows with an intense cherry-red colour. A transparent piece of quartz, however, does not glow at all at this temperature. Explain this phenomenon.

1.5. Show that the total radiation emitted by a "grey" portion $\Delta\sigma$ of the wall of a closed cavity does not differ in any way from that emitted by the "black" portions of the wall, provided that all parts of the cavity are in thermal equilibrium.

1.6. Using Wien's law derive the expression for the distribution of energy in the spectrum of a black body at any temperature, given this distribution at one temperature.

1.7. It is evident that the total radiation density should not depend upon whether the spectral distribution of energy is described by ϱ_ν or by ϱ_λ. This imposes the following condition on the distribution functions:

$$\varrho_\nu \, \mathrm{d}\nu = \varrho_\lambda \lambda.$$

Show, using Wien's law, that as a consequence of this condition, the positions of the maxima of the two functions correspond to different wavelengths.

1.8. One way of estimating the temperature of stellar surfaces is to determine the wavelength corresponding to the maximum of the radiation intensity J_λ in a spectrum whose composition is sufficiently close to that of a black body. This wavelength is 0·55 μ (microns) for the sun, 0·35 μ for the North Star and 0·29 μ for Sirius. Calculate the corresponding star temperatures.

1.9. As a black body cools by emitting radiation, the wavelength that corresponds to the maximum ϱ_λ of the spectral distribution of energy is displaced to 5000 Å. Determine by how many degrees the body cools, if its initial temperature is 2000°K.

1.10. A spherical black body 10 cm in diameter is maintained at a constant temperature. Find this temperature, if the radiative power of the body is known to be 15 kcal/min.

1.11. A model black body is made in the form of a cavity with a small aperture 1 cm in diameter. The cavity is heated by an electric coil that dissipates a power of 0·1 kW, 10 per cent of which is scattered outward by the walls of the cavity. Determine the equilibrium temperature of the radiation emerging from the aperture.

1.12. The mass of the sun is 2×10^{33} g, its radius 7×10^{10} cm and its effective surface temperature 5700°K. From the Stefan–Boltzmann law, calculate the mass lost by the sun in one second by radiation. Estimate the time necessary for the mass of the sun to diminish by 1 per cent.

1.13. The pressure inside the sun is estimated to be of the order of 400 million atmospheres. Estimate the temperature corresponding to such a pressure assuming it to result purely from the radiation.

1.14. Assuming that at high temperatures substances follow the ideal gas law, find the temperature at which the radiation pressure is equal to the gas pressure of a hydrogen gas of density $0 \cdot 1 \text{ g/cm}^3$, whose atoms are completely dissociated into protons and electrons (a very hot plasma).

1.15. Calculate C_v, the specific heat at constant volume, of 1 cm³ of thermal radiation in equilibrium at a temperature of $T = 10^{4}°$K.

1.16. (a) Calculate the entropy S of radiation in thermal equilibrium in a volume $v = 1$ cm³ at a temperature $T = 300°$K.

(b) Express S as a function of c_v, the specific heat at constant volume.

1.17. A cavity of volume $v_0 = 1$ litre is filled with black body radiation at room temperature. What will be the change in entropy of the radiation if the cavity is expanded isothermally to n times its original volume ($n = 4$)?

1.18. Explain why the Rayleigh–Jeans law for the spectral emissive power af a black body leads to the "ultraviolet catastrophe".

PLANCK'S LAW. THE QUANTUM NATURE OF LIGHT

1.19. From the distribution function for energy in the black body spectrum ϱ_ν find the expression for the function ϱ_λ.

1.20. Use Planck's distribution for ϱ_λ to find the corresponding expressions for the two limiting cases: $h\nu < kT$ (Rayleigh–Jeans expression) and $h\nu \gg kT$ (Wien's law).

1.21. Find the ratio of the spectral radiation intensities of wavelengths $\lambda_1 = 0.35\,\mu$ and $\lambda_2 = 0.7\,\mu$ in the spectrum J_λ of a black body at a temperature of 6000°K.

1.22. The radiative power was measured over an interval of 5 Å around the maximum of the black body radiation spectrum J_λ at a temperature $T = 5000°$K. An interval of the spectrum around a wavelength twice as long as λ_{max} has equal radiative power. Determine the width of the second interval.

1.23. Show that the following thermodynamical laws are consequence of Planck's radiation law:

(a) The Stefan–Boltzmann law for the specific radiative power;

(b) The maximum spectral emissivity in the spectrum ϱ_λ of a black body is proportional to the fifth power of the absolute temperature;

(c) The radiative power of the long wavelength portion of the spectrum ϱ_λ is proportional to the first power of the absolute temperature.

1.24. Use Planck's radiation law to express the constant σ in the Stefan–Boltzmann law in terms of the universal constants h, c, k and find its numerical value.

Hint: In making the calculation use the numerical values of the integrals given in Appendix 6.

1.25. Use Planck's law to derive the constant $\lambda_{max}\,T$ in Wien's displacement law in terms of the universal constants h, c, k. Find its approximate numerical value.

1.26. (a) Show that for the energy distribution function $\varrho_\nu(T)$ in the radiation spectrum of a black body, a relation similar to Wien's displacement law is valid, that is $\nu_{max}/T = b'$ where ν_{max} is the radiation frequency corresponding to the maximum of the function ϱ_ν for a given temperature T and b' is a constant.

(b) Find the numerical value of the constant b'. Show that $b' = c/b$, where c is the velocity of light and b the constant in Wien's displacement law.

1.27. Using Planck's radiation law, find the wavelength for which the black body distribution function, ϱ_λ, reaches its maximum value, if $T = 6000°$K.

1.28. Near what frequency ν_0 does the spectral radiation intensity J_ν of an ideal black body depend most strongly on the frequency ν (for a given temperature T)?

1.29. The specific radiative power of the surface of a black body at $T = 2000°K$ is equal to $I = 91.2$ W/cm^2. Hence, determine the value of Planck's constant assuming the values of the velocity of light and of Boltzmann's constant to be known.

Hint: In calculating the value of Planck's constant use the numerical values of the integrals given in Appendix 6.

1.30. Find the energy density of black body radiation in an interval of the spectrum ϱ_λ from $\lambda = 0$ to $\lambda_0 = 3\,\mu$. Assume that $\lambda_0 \ll \lambda_{max}$ and that the radiation temperature is $T = 500°K$.

1.31. At what temperature T will that portion of the intensity, J_λ, of black body radiation contained in the visible part of the spectrum, i.e. from $\lambda_1 = 0.4\,\mu$ to $\lambda_2 = 0.76\,\mu$, be a maximum relative to the total intensity?

1·32. Calculate the relative change in the total number of quanta in a cavity filled with thermal radiation in equilibrium as the absolute temperature of the cavity is changed by a factor of k. (For example, chose $k = 2$.)

1.33. Determine the total number of quanta per cm^3 in a cavity filled with radiation in thermal equilibrium at $t = 0°C$.

Hint: Use the numerical values of the integrals in Appendix 6.

1.34. Calculate the average energy of the quanta in the spectrum of a black body at a temperature of $T = 1000°K$.

Hint: Use the numerical values of the integrals given in Appendix 6.

1.35. Show that the maxima of the distribution function of energy ϱ_ν and of the number of quanta n_ν in the spectrum of a black body correspond to different frequencies. Plot out the approximate forms of these functions in a single diagram.

1.36. From Wien's law for the energy distribution in the spectrum of black body radiation:

$$J_\nu = A\,\nu^3\,e^{-a\nu/T},$$

where A and a are certain constants ($a = 4.8 \times 10^{-11}$ sec . deg), calculate the average value of the frequency of radiation in the solar spectrum ($T = 5700°K$).

1.37. According to Planck's original theory the energy of an oscillator can be represented by

$$E = nh\nu,$$

where n is the number of quanta of energy $h\nu$. Assuming that the probability distribution for occupation of the oscillators is given by Boltzmann's law, compute the mean energy of an oscillator for a given temperature T.

1.38. According to quantum theory the mean energy of a quantum oscillator corresponding to the frequency ν and the absolute temperature T, is given by

$$\overline{E} = \frac{h\nu}{2} + \frac{h\nu}{e^{h\nu/kT} - 1}.$$

(a) Show that for a sufficiently high temperature this expression becomes equal to the classical one. Give the order of magnitude of this temperature.

(b) Sketch a graph of the functions $\overline{E}_\nu(T)$ and $\overline{E}_T(\nu)$.

2. CORPUSCULAR PROPERTIES OF LIGHT

1. The relation between the energy E and the frequency ν of a photon is

$$E = h\nu,$$

where h is Planck's constant.

2. The relation between the momentum p and the wavelength λ of a photon is

$$p = \frac{h}{\lambda}.$$

3. Einstein's law for photoemission from a solid surface is

$$h\nu = A + \frac{mv^2_{max}}{2},$$

where v_{max} is the maximum velocity of the photoelectrons' m the electron mass, and A the electronic work function.

4. The expression describing the Compton scattering of light is:

$$\Delta\lambda = 2\frac{h}{mc}\sin^2\frac{\varphi}{2},$$

where $\Delta\lambda$ is the change of wavelength of the photons scattered at an angle φ to the original direction, and m is the rest mass of the electron.

5. Čerenkov effect: a charged particle moving in a medium with a constant velocity v, greater than the phase velocity of light c' in this medium (i.e., $v > c'$), gives rise to a narrow cone of radiation with an opening angle ϑ to the direction of its motion, for which

$$\cos\vartheta = \frac{c'}{v}.$$

Here $c' = c/n$, where c is the velocity of light in vacuum; n is the refractive index of the medium.

6. The fundamental relation between the total energy E, the momentum p and the rest mass m_0 of a relativistic particle is:

$$E = \frac{m_0 c^2}{\sqrt{1 - \beta^2}},$$

$$E^2 = p^2 c^2 + m_0^2 c^4,$$

where $\beta = v/c$; v is the velocity of the particle.

ENERGY, MOMENTUM AND MASS OF A PHOTON

2.1. Calculate the wavelength and the momentum of a photon with an energy equal to the rest energy of an electron.

2.2. At what temperature does the mean energy of a molecule of an ideal gas become equal to the mean energy of a photon corresponding to the radiation of:
(a) The human body ($\lambda = 10\,\mu$);
(b) Visible light ($\lambda = 0.6\,\mu$)?

2.3. At what temperature will the average momentum of a thermal neutron be equal to the momentum of an X-ray photon of wavelength $\lambda = 1$ Å?

2.4. A monochromatic parallel beam of light passes normally through a long narrow rectangular slit and forms a diffraction pattern on a screen. Find the energy and the momentum of the photons, assuming that the first diffraction minimum appears at an angle of $\varphi = 6°$ to the direction of the beam. The width of the slit is $b = 5$ mm.

2.5. To resolve two spectral lines in the second order spectrum when the diffraction grating is normal to the incident plane beam of light, a grating with a number of lines not less than $N = 10^4$ has to be used. Estimate the relative difference in the energy of the photons corresponding to the two spectral lines.

2.6. Show that the pressure of light flux incident on a reflecting surface with a given intensity J does not depend upon the composition of its spectrum.

2.7. A parallel flux of light of intensity $J = 3$ cal/cm² min . falls normally on a absolutely dull plane surface with unit reflection coefficient. What is the pressure exerted by the flux on the surface?

2.8. In the classical investigations of P. N. Lebedev on the experimental determination of light pressure, a beam of light was directed on the small blades of a very sensitive torsion suspension, represented schematically in Fig. 1. The centres of the small blades are at a distance of 0·9 cm from the axis. Assuming that the tor-

FIG. 1

sion modulus of the filament A is $D = 5 \times 10^{-4}$ erg/rad, determine the angle of twist of the small mirror C when the total flux of luminous energy incident on the blackened blades B is $W = 2$ cal/min.

2.9. Use the corpuscular properties of light to show that for black body radiation $p = \varrho/3$, where p is the pressure and ϱ the volume density of radiation.

2.10. The fact that photons have inertial mass (the pressure of light) leads to the assumption that this mass should also manifest itself as gravitational mass. As a consequence of this we should observe the so-called "red shift" of the spectral lines of stars.

Calculate the magnitude of the relative line displacement in the spectrum of the sun when the earth is at aphelion or at perihelion. The radius of the sun is $R = 696,000$ km and its mass is $1·97 \times 10^{33}$ g.

2.11. Under what conditions can one observe an absence of displacement of spectral lines in a stellar spectrum? Determine the radial velocity of such a star, assuming that its mass M and its diameter D are known.

2.12. A charged particle moves with a constant velocity v in a medium whose refractive index is n. Applying the laws of conservation of energy and momentum to the process of emission of pho-

tons by the particle (the Čerenkov effect), derive the relation between the angle ϑ at which the radiation is emitted and its frequency ν. Show that radiation is emitted only when $v > c'$, where
c' is the phase velocity of light in the medium.

Hint: Take into account that the particle is relativistic and that
the momentum of the photon in the medium is $p = h\nu/c'$.

2.13. (a) An electron and a proton move with a constant velocity
in a medium whose refractive index is $n = 1\cdot6$. For what values
of the kinetic energy of the particles does the Čerenkov radiation
appear?

(b) Calculate the mass and identify the particles which start to
emit radiation on moving through a medium with a refractive index $n = 1\cdot5$ when their kinetic energy is greater than 38 MeV.

PHOTOELECTRIC EFFECT

2.14. According to classical electrodynamics an oscillator placed
in the path of an electromagnetic wave of wavelength λ absorbs
the energy that falls on a surface element of area $\Delta\sigma \cong \lambda^2$. Using
this, estimate for how long one would have to illuminate an
atom with radiation of wavelength $\lambda = 350$ mμ and intensity
$J = 2 \times 10^{-6}$ erg/cm^2 . sec so that it would emit a photoelectron
with a binding energy equal to the energy of the quantum of the
given radiation. How would you expect the process of emission
of photoelectrons to occur under these conditions?

2.15. A pulse of radiation, consisting of 5×10^4 light quanta of
wavelength $\lambda = 0\cdot3$ μ, falls on a photosensitive surface, whose sen-
sitivity for in this wavelength region is $J = 4\cdot5$ ma/W. Find the
number of photoelectrons liberated by the pulse.

2.16. Explain why, even for monochromatic illumination, there
is a velocity dispersion of photoelectrons?

2.17. What are the maximum velocities of the photoelectrons
when surfaces of platinum and caesium are illuminated by the
resonance lines of:

(a) mercury ($\lambda = 1850$ Å);

(b) calcium ($\lambda = 4227$ Å).

The work functions for various metals are given in Appendix 3.

2.18. A small copper ball suspended *in vacuo* is illuminated by monochromatic light of wavelength $0.2 \, \mu$. What is the maximum potential the ball will acquire by losing photoelectrons?

2.19. A metal surface is illuminated by light of wavelengths 2790 Å and 2450 Å, the corresponding retarding potential being 0·66 V and 1·26 V respectively. The electron charge and the velocity of light are assumed to be known. Hence obtain the values of Planck's constant and of the work function for this metal.

2.20. A quantum of wavelength $\lambda = 232 \, m\mu$ liberates a photoelectron from the surface of a platinum electrode. Using the laws of energy and momentum conservation (cf. the Compton effect) determine the total momentum acquired by the photoelectrons, assuming that it is emitted in a direction opposite to that of the incident quantum.

2.21. As a result of the action of an incident quantum of radiation of wavelength $\lambda = 2720$ Å a microscopic tungsten particle emits a photoelectron at right angles to the incident quantum. Determine the magnitude and the direction of the momentum transferred to the particle as the result of its absorbing the quantum and emitting a photoelectron with a velocity which is 2 per cent of the maximum possible under these conditions.

2.22. A photoelectron, liberated by a gamma quantum from the K shell of a tungsten atom (ionization energy $E_i = 69.3$ keV), moves in a medium with refractive index $n = 1.4$. Find what the wavelength of the gamma quantum must be for the photoelectron to start to emit light (Čerenkov effect).

2.23. The work function A of an electron in a metal is defined by the difference $W_n - W_k$, where W_n is the depth of the potential well and W_k the maximum kinetic energy of the electrons in the metal (Fig. 2). Theory shows that

$$W_k = \frac{h^2}{2m} \left(\frac{3n}{8\pi} \right)^{2/3},$$

where h is Planck's constant, m the mass of the electron and n the number of conduction electrons per unit volume. Determine the depth of the potential well for potassium, if the number of conduction electrons is one per atom and the photoelectric threshold for potassium is 5770 Å.

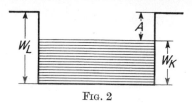

FIG. 2

2.24. A vacuum photoelectric cell consists of two plates, one of copper and one of platinum, short-circuited externally. When one of these is illuminated (which one?) the emitted photoelectrons fall on a retarding electric field set up by the external contact potential difference. Determine the value of the threshold wavelength of the light for which the photoelectrons begin to reach the opposite plate (see Appendix 3, for work functions of platinum and copper).

2.25. A photoelectric cell consists of two different electrodes, one of which is illuminated by monochromatic light of 185 mμ wavelength. The photoelectric current starts flowing only when an accelerating voltage of 0·4 V is applied externally. It is also known that the external contact potential difference between the two electrodes is 1·81 V. Determine the work function for the illuminated electrode.

2.26. When a potential of 62 kV is applied to an X-ray tube the wavelength of the short wave limit of the continuous X-ray spectrum is found to be 0·2 Å. Assuming that the electron charge and the velocity of light are known, determine the value of Planck's constant.

THE COMPTON EFFECT

2.27. The Compton effect is observed when photons are scattered by free electrons.

(a) Which electrons in a substance may be treated as being free?

(b) Why is the Compton effect not observed when visible light is scattered?

2.28. Explain the following features of the Compton effect:

(a) The increase in the intensity of the shifted component which occurs as the atomic number of the substance decreases, and also as the scattering angle increases;

(b) The fact that the magnitude of the shift is independent of the nature of the scattering substance;

(c) The presence of the undisplaced component.

2.29. Compare the maximum change of wavelength in the Compton scattering of photons on free electrons with that for scattering on protons.

2.30. The wavelength of an incident quantum is equal to 0·03 Å. What is the energy of the Compton recoil electron when the quantum is scattered at 60°, 90° and 180° respectively?

2.31. After a 0·8 MeV photon is scattered on a free electron the wavelength of the scattered photon is found to be equal to the Compton wavelength. What is the angle of scattering of the photon?

2.32. Figure 3 shows the energy spectrum of electrons emitted when a sample of one of the light elements is illuminated by hard monochromatic X-ray radiation.

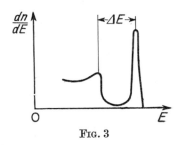

FIG. 3

(a) Explain this spectrum and the origin of the electrons that give rise to the two maxima.

(b) Determine the wavelength of the radiation, the energy of the photoelectrons, and the maximum energy of the Compton recoil electrons assuming that $\Delta E = 181$ keV.

2.33. In a certain experiment on the Compton scattering of light it was observed that the scattered quantum came off at an angle φ to its original direction of motion, while the recoil electron described a circular path of radius ϱ in a magnetic field of strength H. Find the wavelength of the incident quantum, in the two cases:

(a) $\varphi = 60°$, $\varrho = 1·5$ cm, $H = 200$ oe.

(b) $\varphi = 90°$, $\varrho = 2$ cm, $H = 3000$ oe.

2.34. From the law of conservation of momentum and the Compton effect formula, find the relation between φ, the angle of scattering of the photon and ψ, the angle by which the recoil electron is scattered.

2.35. Determine the angle between the directions of motion of the scattered photon and of the recoil electron, assuming that the Compton shift is 0·012 Å and the wavelength of the incident photon is 0·05 Å.

2.36. A photon that corresponds to the short wave limit of the continuous X-ray spectrum when the potential on the X-ray tube is $U = 60$ kV undergoes Compton scattering at an angle $\varphi = 120°$ and then knocks out a photoelectron from the K-shell of a molybdenum atom. Calculate the energy of the photoelectron at a distance from the atom, assuming the ionization energy of the K-shell of this atom to be $E = 20$ keV.

2.37. (a) What causes the broadening of both component lines in the Compton effect?

(b) In observing the scattering at an angle of $\varphi = 50°$ of radiation with an initial wavelength of 0·6 Å, the width of each component is found to be approximately equal to the magnitude of the compton shift. Assuming that the broadening of the lines is due only to Doppler effect, estimate the order of magnitude of the velocity of the free electrons in this material.

2.38. Using the conservation laws of energy and momentum, show that a free electron

(a) cannot completely absorb the energy of a photon;

(b) cannot emit energy.

3. THE RUTHERFORD–BOHR ATOM

1. The angle, measured with respect to its initial direction, through which a charged particle is scattered by a nucleus, considered as a point charge at rest is given by the following expression:

$$\tan\frac{\vartheta}{2} = \frac{q_1 q_2}{2 E p}.$$

where q_1, q_2 are the charges of the incoming particle and the scattering nucleus respectively, E the kinetic energy of the incident particle, p its impact parameter.

2. Rutherford's expression for the scattering of charged particles is:

$$\frac{\Delta N}{N} = n \left(\frac{q_1 q_2}{4 E}\right)^2 \frac{\Delta \omega}{\sin^4 \vartheta/2},$$

where $\Delta N/N$ is the relative number of particles scattered per unit time into an element of solid angle $\Delta\omega$ at an angle ϑ with the original direction of motion of the particles; n is the number of nuclei of the scatterer per unit area; q_1, q_2 are the charges of the incident particles and of the scattering nuclei; E is the kinetic energy of the incident particles.

3. The mass thickness of a foil is defined as the product ϱd (g/cm²), where σ is the density and d the thickness of the foil.

4. The Bohr postulates are

$$h \nu = E_2 - E_1,$$

$$l_n = \frac{h}{2\pi} n,$$

where E_2 and E_1 are the energies of an electron in the states with quantum numbers n_2 and n_1, the transition between which occurs with the emission (or absorption) of a light quantum of frequency ν; l_n is the angular momentum of an electron in the nth orbit; h is Planck's constant.

5. The generalized Balmer formula for hydrogen-like ions is

$$\bar{\nu} = RZ^2 \left(\frac{1}{n_1^2} - \frac{1}{n_2^2} \right) \mathrm{cm}^{-1},$$

where $\bar{\nu}$ is the wave number ($\bar{\nu} = 1/\lambda$, λ is the wavelength of the light); n_1 and n_2 are the orbital quantum numbers; R is Rydberg's constant.

6. The Rydberg constant depends upon the mass M of a nucleus as follows:

$$R = \frac{R_\infty}{1 + \dfrac{m}{M}},$$

where

$$R_\infty = \frac{2\pi^2 m e^4}{c h^3};$$

here m and e are the mass and charge of the electron respectively; M is the mass of the nucleus; R_∞ is Rydberg's constant for $M \to \infty$, c is the velocity of light, and h is Planck's constant.

RUTHERFORD'S SCATTERING FORMULA

3.1. A uranium nucleus at rest undergoes a head-on collision with an incoming proton whose velocity at a great distance from the nucleus is $2 \cdot 25 \times 10^9$ cm/sec. What is the distance of least approach of the particles?

3.2. After passing through a thin gold foil a $5 \cdot 4$ MeV alpha particle is found to be deflected by $60°$ from its original direction. Calculate the impact parameter for this scattering event, assuming the nuclei behave as point charges, and compare it to the effective radius of the target nucleus.

3.3. After colliding with a thorium nucleus at rest a $0 \cdot 5$ MeV proton was deflected by $30°$ relative to its original direction of motion. Find the distance of minimum approach of the two particles during the collision.

3.4. (a) Why is it that in confirming Rutherford's formula by experiment the scattering substance must be in the form of a thin foil?

(b) What conclusions can be drawn from the fact that the scattering of charged particles in passing through a material occurs according to Rutherford's formula? When does one observe a disagreement with the formula?

3.5. The scattering of protons of kinetic E on a thin thorium target is represented well by Rutherford's expression up to $E = 4.3$ MeV. Estimate from this result the range of the nuclear forces for this case.

3.6. In experiments on the scattering of alpha particles into small angles ϑ a sharp departure from the Rutherford formula is observed. What causes it?

3.7. Construct the polar diagram for scattering of alpha particles according to Rutherford's expression $\varrho(\vartheta) = dN/Nd\omega$ in the angle interval from 60° to 180°.

3.8. A narrow beam of alpha particles with an intensity of 5×10^3 particles/sec and an energy of 3 MeV, falls perpendicularly upon a gold foil $1\,\mu$ thick. How many of the scattered alpha particles will be registered in the course of 10 min in the angle interval 59°–61°?

3.9. A narrow beam of 3.5 MeV alpha particles strikes the surface of a silver foil of a mass thickness of 1.05 mg/cm² at an angle of $\varphi = 60°$. The relative intensity of the scattered alpha particles, entering a counter with an aperture 0.6 cm² in area placed at a distance $L = 12$ cm from the scattering portion of the foil, amounts to $\eta = 2.9 \times 10^{-5}$ when observed at an angle $\vartheta = 20°$ with respect to the original direction of the beam. Find the charge of a silver nucleus.

3.10. The fraction of 6 MeV protons scattered by a gold foil into angles greater than 60° is equal to 2×10^{-5}. Determine the thickness of the foil.

3.11. A narrow beam of alpha particles, accelerated by a potential $U = 4$ MV, falls normally on a uranium foil of mass thickness $\varrho d = 1.9$ mg/cm². A fraction 0.5 per cent of the particles is scattered into the angle interval from $\vartheta_1 = 10°$ to $\vartheta_2 = 30°$.

(a) Determine Avogadro's number.

(b) Find the relative number of protons which would be scattered by the same foil within the same angle interval, assuming that their energy corresponds to the same potential difference $U = 4$ MV.

3.12. (a) Find the value of the differential cross-section of the tantalum nucleus obtained by averaging the exact differential cross section for scattering of a beam of 1 MeV protons over a range of scattering angles from 50° to 60°.

(b) What proton energy will give the same average differential cross-section as above, when the averaging is made over the interval 30° to 60°?

3.13. A beam of alpha particles of energy E is scattered in passing through a lead foil of mass thickness 2·3 mg/cm². Find the differential scattering cross-section for the lead nucleus, assuming that a fraction $\eta = 10^{-4}$ of the total beam is scattered into an interval of angles $\Delta \vartheta$.

THE BOHR THEORY OF THE ATOM

3.14. Use the Thomson model[1] of an atom to determine the magnitude of the electric dipole moment of a one-electron atom in a constant electric field of strength $E = 600$ V/cm. Assume the radius of the atom to be $r_0 = 10^{-8}$ cm.

3.15. Use the Thomson model for an atom with one electron to calculate the frequency of incident light for which the absorption (or scattering) of energy by the atoms of the medium is at a maxiumum. The radius of the atom is $r_0 = 10^{-8}$ cm. Neglect damping.

3.16. Why is the Thomson model of the atom inconsistent?

3.17. According to classical electrodynamics an electron moving with an acceleration a radiates the energy

$$E = \frac{2\,e^2}{3\,c^3}\,a^2,$$

per unit time, where e is the electron charge, c the velocity of light. Starting from this expression, compare the radiation per unit time of an electron in an orbit of radius $r = 10^{-8}$ cm with that in an orbit whose radius is half as large.

3.18. Estimate the "life time" of an atom from classical arguments, using only the assumption that the total acceleration of an electron in an orbit is always equal to the centripetal acceleration. Use the expression for the energy radiated given in the preceding problem. The initial radius of the electron orbit is of the order of 10^{-8} cm.

3.19. Figure 4 shows the ampere–volt characteristic obtained in the Frank–Hertz experiments on the inelastic scattering of electrons on the atoms of mercury vapour.

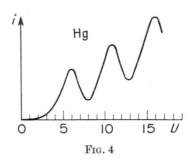

FIG. 4

(a) Explain the nature of the curve.

(b) Determine from the diagram the excitation potential U_1 of a mercury atom. Can one estimate U_1 from the position of the first maximum of the curve alone?

(c) Find the wavelength of the light emitted by the mercury vapour when its atoms are excited by the bombarding electrons to the first energy level. To what part of the spectrum does the emitted spectral line belong?

3.20. (a) Find the numerical values of the potential, the kinetic and the total energies of an electron in the first and second orbits of a hydrogen atom.

(b) When is the total energy of an electron in a hydrogen atom equal to half its potential energy?

(c) Find the ratio of the Coulomb force and the gravitational force of attraction between the electron and the nucleus of a hydrogen atom.

3.21. Estimate the factor by which the radius of an orbit in a hydrogen atom, initially in the ground state, will increase when it is excited by a 12·09 eV quantum.

3.22. Express the frequency of revolution of the electron about the nucleus of a hydrogen atom as a function of E, the total energy of the electron (set the potential energy equal to zero at infinity).

3.23. Calculate the frequencies of revolution of the electron in the first and second orbits of a hydrogen atom and the frequency of the quantum corresponding to the transition between the two orbits. Compare the two results.

3.24. Show that the following inequality holds for the frequency ν of a quantum emitted by a hydrogen atom

$$\nu_n > \nu > \nu_{n+1},$$

where ν_n and ν_{n+1} are the frequencies of revolution of the electron in the two neighbouring orbits between which the transition occurs. Show also that $\nu \to \nu_n$ for $n \to \infty$.

3.25. (a) Use Bohr's theory to determine the magnetic moment of an electron moving on the nth orbit of a hydrogen atom. Show that the ratio of the magnetic moment to the angular momentum is constant for all orbits.

(b) Calculate the angular velocity and the total energy of the electron which in its motion in a certain orbit of a hydrogen atom has a magnetic moment of $2 \cdot 78 \times 10^{20}$ erg/gauss.

3.26. A hydrogen atom in the ground state absorbs a quantum of light wavelength $\lambda = 1026$ Å. Determine the resulting change in the orbital magnetic moment of the electron.[2]

3.27. Calculate and draw to scale a diagram representing of the first four energy levels of the hydrogen atom. Determine the number of possible transitions and the wavelengths of the corresponding spectral lines. To what series do they belong?

3.28. How many lines are observed in the absorption spectrum of atomic hydrogen within the wavelength range from 945 to 1100 Å?

3.29. Estimate the change in the angular momentum of an electron in a hydrogen atom when it emits a spectral line of wavelength 12,818 Å. This line belongs to the Paschen series.

3.30. Find the quantum number of the excited state of a hydrogen atom, given that in the transition to the ground state it emits one photon of wavelength $972 \cdot 5$ Å.

3.31. Determine the value of the first excitation potential of the hydrogen atom and also its ionization potential. Calculate the wavelengths, frequencies and wave numbers of the corresponding quanta.

3.32. The wavelengths of two spectral lines of the Balmer series are 4861 Å and 4102 Å. Using the Ritz combination principle determine to which series the spectral line, whose wave number is equal to the wave number difference of the given lines, belongs. What it its wavelength?

3.33. In the atomic hydrogen spectrum the spacing of the first two Balmer lines is 5326 cm^{-1}. Using this fact determine Rydberg constant.

3.34. The wavelengths of the principal Lyman series line and of the Balmer series limit in the atomic hydrogen spectrum are respectively 1215 and 3650 Å. The values of the velocity of light and of Planck's constant are also assumed to be known. Find the ionization potential of the hydrogen atom.

3.35. The difference in wavelengths between the principal lines of the Balmer and the Lyman series in the spectrum of atomic hydrogen is 5347 Å. Hence find the value of Planck's constant, assuming the mass of the electron, its charge and the velocity of light to be known.

3.36. In observing the spectrum of atomic hydrogen by means of a diffraction grating with a period $d = 2\mu$ it is found that one of the spectral lines of the Balmer series in the kth order ($k = 2$) corresponds to the diffraction angle $\varphi = 29° \, 05'$ (Fig. 5). What is the quantum number of the atomic energy level giving rise to this line?

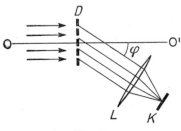

Fig. 5

3.37. What is the minimum number of lines necessary on a diffraction grating for the resolution in the second order spectrum of the first 30 spectral lines of the Balmer series of atomic hydrogen?

3.38. A quantum of light with an energy of 15 eV knocks out a photoelectron from a hydrogen atom in its ground state. What will be the velocity of the ejected electron at a great distance from the nucleus?

3.39. Apply the laws of conservation of energy and momentum to the emission of photons by an atom in motion to obtain the expression for the Doppler shift in the non-relativistic case.

3.40. The wavelength of a potassium line is 3969 Å when the line is emitted from sources on the earth. The red shift for the same line when observed in the spectra of certain distant galaxies amounts to 80 Å. Assuming that this shift is entirely due to the Doppler effect, determine

(a) the radial velocity with which these galaxies are moving away from us;

(b) the wavelength in the spectra of these galaxies corresponding to the principal Lyman series line for singly ionized helium.

3.41. In observing a beam of excited hydrogen atoms at an angle of 45° to the direction of their motion, the wavelength of the spectral line corresponding to the transition $n_2 = 2 \to n_1 = 1$ is λ 1215·18 Å. Estimate the velocity of the hydrogen atoms, assuming that Rydberg's constant is $R = 109677·6 \text{ cm}^{-1}$.

3.42. Determine the quantum numbers of those energy levels (orbits) of hydrogen like ions which are such that the transitions between them, give rise to photons with the same frequencies as the lines of the Lyman series of atomic hydrogen.

3.43. What is the minimum velocity of approach of a hydrogen atom H and a helium atom ion He$^+$ necessary for the quantum of light produced by He$^+$ in the transition $n_2 = 3 \to n_1 = 2_1$ to excite the hydrogen atom?

3.44. Because of its finite mass, the nucleus of the hydrogen atom is in motion relative to a common centre. Taking this into account, give a more exact solution of the following problem:

(a) Find the expression for the total kinetic energy of the electron–nucleus system;

(b) Prove that in this case the total energy of the system is still equal to half the potential energy, assuming the latter to be zero at infinite separation.

3.45. (a) Taking into account the finite mass of the hydrogen nucleus, derive the generalized Balmer formula and the dependence of Rydberg's constant on the mass of the nucleus.

2*

(b) Find the general expression for the magnetic moment of a hydrogen atom when the motion of its nucleus is taken into account.

3.46. Find the difference between the wavelengths of the principal Lyman series, lines, the first excitation potentials, and the ionization potentials for these following pairs of atoms:
(a) hydrogen and deuterium,
(b) deuterium and tritium.

3.47. Is it possible to observe the doublet structure of the resonance lines of the hydrogen-like ions in a mixture of the following two isotopes:
(a) He^5 and He^6,
(b) Li^5 and Li^6,
by using a spectrometer with a resolving power of 0·003 Å?

3.48. The mass of the hydrogen nucleus is $1·672 \times 10^{-24}$ g and that of the helium nucleus $6·644 \times 10^{-24}$ g. The ratio of their Rydberg constants is $\eta = 0·999593$. Hence find the mass of the electron.

3.49. A system consisting of an electron and a positron moving about a common centre of gravity is called positronium. Calculate the mean distance between the electron and the positron in the ground state and the corresponding ionization potential of positronium. Find also the magnitude of the orbital magnetic moment μ of positronium.

3.50. The mesic hydrogen atom differs from the ordinary hydrogen atom in that instead of an electron there is a μ-meson moving in it. The μ-meson has the same charge as the electron and a mass 210 times greater. For the mesic atom calculate the distance between the meson and the nucleus in the first orbit and the wavelength corresponding to the resonance transition. Compare the values obtained with those for an ordinary hydrogen atom.

3.51. For a mesic hydrogen atom calculate the value of the Rydberg constant, the potential of resonance excitation and the ionization potential, taking into account that the μ-meson mass is 210 times greater than that of the electron.

REFERENCES

1. F. K. RICHTMEYER and E. H. KENNARD, *Introduction to Modern Physics*, McGraw–Hill, 4th Edition, p. 197.
2. For a discussion of the selection rules governing atomic transitions see the above, p. 320.

4. WAVE PROPERTIES OF PARTICLES

1. The de Broglie relations are:

$$\lambda = \frac{h}{p},$$

$$E = h\nu,$$

where λ and ν are the wavelength and the frequency corresponding to the momentum $p = mv$ and the energy E of the particle.

2. The expressions for the phase velocity w and the group velocity g of the de Broglie waves are:

$$w = \frac{\nu}{k},$$

$$g = \frac{d\nu}{dk} = w - \lambda \frac{dw}{d\lambda},$$

where k is the wave number ($k = 1/\lambda$); λ and ν are the wavelength and frequency of the de Broglie waves.

3. The Bragg formula is:

$$2d\sin\vartheta = k\lambda,$$

where d is the distance between the crystal planes, ϑ the glancing angle, and k the order of the spectrum.

4. The Bragg formula, taking into account the refraction of the electron waves in a crystal, is given by:

$$2d\sqrt{n^2 - \cos^2\vartheta} = k\lambda,$$

where n, the refractive index, depends on the energy of the electrons (i.e. on the accelerating potential U_0) and on the internal potential of the crystal U_i [1]:

$$n = \sqrt{1 + \frac{U_i}{U_0}}.$$

5. The resolving power of an apparatus is defined as:

$$d = \frac{\lambda}{2A},$$

where d is the least distance between two lines on the object which can be separated by means of the system; λ is the de Broglie wavelength of the particle; A is the numerical aperture of the objective, and is equal to the product of the refractive index of the medium between the object and the system and the sine of half the angle subtended by rays issuing from a point of the object and incident on the system.

6. The uncertainty relation for the coordinate and the corresponding component of momentum of a particle is:

$$\Delta x \Delta p_x \gtrsim \hbar,$$

where $\hbar$ is Planck's constant divided by 2π

$$(\hbar = h/2\pi = 1\cdot05 \times 10^{-27} \text{ erg. sec}).$$

DE BROGLIE'S HYPOTHESIS.
WAVE PROPERTIES OF PARTICLES

4.1. Write the de Broglie wave function for a freely moving particle, using the parameters ν, k and E, p when
(a) the particle moves along the x-axis;
(b) the particle moves at an arbitrary angle to the coordinate axes.

4.2. Calculate the de Broglie wavelength of an electron, of a hydrogen atom and of a uranium atom, assuming that the kinetic energy of each is 100 eV.

4.3. Determine the de Broglie wavelength of a proton for which its kinetic energy is equal to the rest energy of an electron.

4.4. Find the velocities and the kinetic energies of an electron and of a neutron for which the de Broglie wavelengths are equal to 1 Å.

4.5. An electron moves along a circular path 0·5 cm in radius in a uniform magnetic field of strength $H = 46$ oe. What is the de Broglie wavelength of the electron?

4.6. What is the velocity of an electron with a de Broglie wavelength equal to that of a neutron moving with mean thermal velocity at 0°C?

4.7. At what absolute temperature T will the de Broglie wavelength corresponding to the average velocity of hydrogen molecules in a gas be 0·1 of the mean distance between the molecules? Calculate T for the case that the number of molecules in 1 cm³ is Avogadro's number.

4.8. From the velocity distribution of the molecules of an ideal gas at a certain equilibrium temperature T (the Maxwell distribution) derive the distribution of the molecules as a function of their de Broglie wavelengths.

4.9. From the answer to the preceding problem find the most probable de Broglie wavelength of hydrogen molecules at room temperature.

4.10. What is the rate of change of the de Broglie wavelength of a proton $(d\lambda/dt)$ accelerated by a longitudinal uniform electric field of strength $E = 3000$ V/cm, at the moment when its kinetic energy is 1 keV?

4.11. An electron moves with a velocity v when observed from the laboratory coordinate system $(v \ll c)$.

(a) What will be its de Broglie wavelength and its frequency when observed from a coordinate system moving with a velocity kv in the direction of motion of the electron? Consider the case when $k \ll 1$, $k = 2$, and $k > 2$.

(b) Determine $\Delta\lambda$ and $\Delta\nu$ for $k = 0·5$ and $v = 0·01\,c$, where c is the velocity of light.

4.12. For what energy values can one expect an especially sharp diffraction pattern, if neutrons are scattered on natural crystals with lattice constants in the range from 2·5 to 6·0 Å?

4.13. Derive the general expression for the de Broglie wavelength of a relativistic particle as a function of the accelerating potential.

4.14. For what value of the accelerating potential will the error in determining the de Broglie wavelength, using a non-relativistic approximation, be of order 1 per cent:

(a) for an electron;

(b) for a proton;

(c) for an alpha particle?

4.15. For what value of the kinetic energy is the de Broglie wavelength of an electron equal to its Compton wavelength?

4.16. Electron accelerators with energies up to 6000 MeV are being built in many laboratories in the world in order to study the structure of the atomic nucleus. What is the de Broglie wavelength of these electrons? Why are such high energies needed?

4.17. Show that integer multiples of de Broglie wavelengths correspond to the stationary orbits of a Bohr atom. How many wavelengths fit into each orbit? How does the wavelength depend on the orbital quantum number and the universal constants? Obtain the numerical values of the wavelengths for the first two hydrogen orbits.

4.18. A 1 keV proton is scattered elastically by 90° on a helium nucleus originally at rest. What is the de Broglie wavelength of the scattered proton at a large distance from the atom?

4.19. In one of the Davisson–Germer experiments on the reflection of electrons from a nickel monocrystal the 4th order maximum was observed in a direction forming an angle $\alpha = 55°$ with the direction of the incident 180 eV electrons (see Fig. 6). Calculate

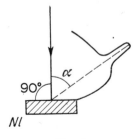

FIG. 6

the interplane distance d, corresponding to such a reflection. Determine also the angle between the crystal planes and the surface of the monocrystal.

4.20. In an experiment by P. S. Tartakovski a beam of monoenergetic electrons, accelerated by a potential difference of 410 V, falls perpendicularly on a thin aluminium foil, which is a polycrystalline structure. On a screen 10 cm from the foil a system of diffraction rings is formed. The diameter of the ring corresponding to the first order reflection from crystal planes with an inter-plane distance d, is 3 cm. Determine d, neglecting the refraction of the electron waves in the foil.

4.21. By allowing a beam of fast 51 keV electrons to pass through a thin copper film, G. P. Thomson observed a Debye-type electron pattern on a screen.

(a) Determine the angle of deflection undergone by the electrons forming the diffraction ring for a 4th order reflection from crystal planes, the distance between which is equal to the lattice constant, i.e. 3·6 Å. To simplify matters neglect the refraction of electron waves inside the film.

(b) How can one show experimentally that the diffraction pattern seen on the screen is due only to the scattered electrons and not to secondary X-ray emission?

4.22. Obtain the dependence of the refractive index of the de Broglie waves upon U_i, the internal potential of a metal, and upon E_0, the kinetic energy of electrons in a vacuum.

4.23. The refractive index of a metal with respect to the vacuum for electron waves of energy 200 eV is 1·03. Determine the internal potential of the metal.

4.24. It is known that when electrons cross a vacuum–metal boundary only the normal component of their momentum is changed. Find the refractive index of the electron waves, the angle of refraction, and the velocity of the electrons, in platinum, assuming that the electron beam strikes the surface at an angle of $\vartheta = 45°$ with an energy $E = 120$ eV. The internal potential of platinum is $U_i = 12$ V.

4.25. Derive the Bragg formula, taking into account the fact that the refractive index of electron waves in a crystal is not unity.

4.26. The angles of incidence and of reflection of a beam of electrons from a system of parallel crystal planes is 30°. The 4th order reflection maximum is observed for an accelerating potential difference of 101·8 V. Show that the refractive index of the electron waves in this case is equal to 1·03. Calculate the distance between crystal planes corresponding to this reflection.

4.27. Calculate the theoretical magnitude of the resolving power to be expected in an electron microscope when an accelerating voltage of 100 kV is applied, the numerical aperture being 0·1. What will the de Broglie wavelength of the electrons be in this case?

4.28. A plane flux of relativistic electrons falls perpendicularly on an electron lens with an aperture 1 mm in diameter. For what energy of the electrons is the resolving power of the system equal to $A = 1 \cdot 10^8$?

Note.[2] $A = 1/\psi$, where ψ is the angle corresponding to the first dark diffraction ring in the focal plane of the lens satisfying the condition $D \sin \psi = 1 \cdot 22 \lambda$, where λ is the de Broglie wavelength.

4.29. From the expression defining the group velocity of a particle show that $g = v$, where v is the velocity of the particle. Do this for the non-relativistic ($v \ll c$) and the relativistic ($v \sim c$) cases.

THE UNCERTAINTY RELATIONS

4.30. An electron with a kinetic energy of the order of 10 eV, is located inside a spherical metal particle 10^{-6} cm³ in volume. Using the uncertainty relations find the relative error determining the velocity of the electron.

4.31. The position of the centre of gravity of a spherical pellet whose mass is equal to 2 mg can be determined with an accuracy of up to 2μ. Has the uncertainty relation any practical significance in determining the velocity of this pellet?

4.32. In order to determine whether an electron belongs to a given atom, its position must be determined with an accuracy of 10^{-8} cm. Compare the uncertainty in determining the velocity of the electron, for example in the first Bohr orbit of a hydrogen atom, with the magnitude of the velocity itself.

4.33. For what relative error in measuring the angular momentum of an electron in the first Bohr orbit will its angle coordinate prove to be totally indeterminate?

4.34. Estimate from the uncertainty relation the linear dimensions of atoms and nuclei, assuming that the energy related to the uncertainty of the momentum of electrons in atoms and of nucleons in nuclei is 10 eV and 1 MeV respectively.

4.35. An atom emits a photon of wavelength $\lambda = 5500$ Å. It is known that the emission time τ is of the order of 10^{-8} sec.

(a) With what accuracy can the photon be localized in the direction of its motion?

(b) Starting from the uncertainty relation for energy ($\Delta E\tau \approx \hbar$) estimate the error in the determination of the wavelength.

4.36. The track of a particle in a cloud chamber consists of a chain of vapour droplets about 10^{-4} cm in diameter. Can the deviation from the laws of motion of classical mechanics be detected in observing the track of a 1 keV electron?

4.37. A collimating slit is placed in the path of a parallel beam of 0·06 eV hydrogen atoms. At a distance $l = 1$ m away from the slit there is a screen. Estimate the width of the slit, d, which makes the width of the image of the beam on the screen a minimum. What will the value of d be in the case of electrons, assuming the same values for E and l?

4.38. An electron is "trapped" in a uniform rectangular potential well of width l with absolutely impenetrable walls. From the uncertainty relations estimate the order of magnitude of the minimum possible energy of the electron when:
(a) $l \approx 10^{-8}$ cm.
(b) $l \approx 10^{-12}$ cm.

4.39. Estimate the uncertainty in the momentum of an electron trapped in a uniform potential field.

$$U(x) = \begin{cases} \infty, x \leqq 0, \\ eEx, x > 0, \end{cases}$$

where $E = 3 \times 10^7$ V/cm, assuming that its energy is the least possible.

4.40. A particle of mass m moves in a potential well of the form $U = k|x|^3$. Use the uncertainty relations to estimate the linear dimensions of the region where the given particle could be found when it has the least possible energy.

4.41. Use the uncertainty relations to estimate the order of magnitude of the least possible energy of a harmonic oscillator of frequency ν.

4.42. Use the uncertainty relations to estimate the total energy of an electron located close to the nucleus of a light atom of atomic number Z. Test the correctness of your result for hydrogen.
Note. Electrons in light atoms are non-relativistic.

4.43. Use the uncertainty relation to estimate the energy of the ground state of the helium atom.

4.44. A parallel beam of monoenergetic electrons of energy E falls perpendicularly on a diaphragm that has a narrow, long rectangular slit d cm wide. Find the distribution of the particles and the position of the first minimum in the diffraction pattern on a sreen placed parallel to the diaphragm at a distance L from it.

4.45. Show that measurement of the coordinate of a particle by means of a slit of width d will give rise to an uncertainty Δp in determining the momentum such that the product $d \cdot \Delta p$ satisfies the uncertainty relation.

4.46. Show that the uncertainty relation is a consequence of the wave properties of micro-particles. To prove this, consider a wave packet, i.e. a group of waves that has a narrow spectral range $(\lambda_0 - \Delta\lambda, \lambda_0 + \Delta\lambda)$. The region where the probability of finding a particle noticeably differs from zero is taken to be the width of the packet.

REFERENCE

1. Z. G. PINSKER, *Electron Diffraction*, English translation, Butterworth 1953, p.12.
2. cf. *op. cit.*, p. 45.

5. THE SCHRÖDINGER EQUATION

1. The general (time dependent) Schrödinger equation is:

$$i\hbar\frac{\partial\Psi}{\partial t} = -\frac{\hbar^2}{2m}\nabla^2\Psi + U\Psi,$$

where $\psi(x, y, z, t)$ is the total wave function of the particle; m is its mass; ∇^2 is the Laplace operator (see 3 below); $u(x, y, z, t)$ is the potential function.

2. The Schrödinger equation for stationary states, when U does not depend explicitly on time, is:

$$\nabla^2\psi + \frac{2m}{\hbar^2}(E - U)\psi = 0,$$

where $\psi(x, y, z)$ is the spatial part of the wave function, E the total energy of the particle, $U(x, y, z)$ its potential energy.

3. The Laplace operator expressed in cartesian coordinates is

$$\nabla^2 = \frac{\partial^2}{\partial x^2} + \frac{\partial^2}{\partial y^2} + \frac{\partial^2}{\partial z^2},$$

in cylindrical coordinates:

$$\nabla^2 = \frac{1}{r}\frac{\partial}{\partial r}\left(r\frac{\partial}{\partial r}\right) + \frac{1}{r^2}\frac{\partial^2}{\partial\varphi^2} + \frac{\partial^2}{\partial z^2},$$

in spherical coordinates:

$$\nabla^2 = \frac{1}{r^2}\frac{\partial}{\partial r}\left(r^2\frac{\partial}{\partial r}\right) + \frac{1}{r^2\sin\vartheta}\frac{\partial}{\partial\vartheta}\left(\sin\vartheta\frac{\partial}{\partial\vartheta}\right) + \frac{1}{r^2\sin^2\vartheta}\frac{\partial^2}{\partial\varphi^2}.$$

4. Physically admissible solutions of the Schrödinger equation must satisfy the following conditions: the wave function ψ must be finite†, continuous and single valued.

† More precisely, the function should be quadratically integrable, i.e. it must satisfy the condition $\int|\psi|^2\mathrm{d}^3x = 1$, where the integral is taken over all space.

5. The average value of quantity $f(x)$ in a stationary state described by the normalized wave function $\psi(x)$ is, by definition:

$$f = \int\limits_{-\infty}^{+\infty} f(x)\psi^*\psi\,\mathrm{d}x,$$

where ψ^* is the complex conjugate of ψ. (The formula is given for one-dimension, but generalizes straight away to any number of dimensions.)

5.1. A free particle of mass m moves in the direction of the positive x-axis with a velocity $v\,(v \ll c)$. Write down the time dependent Schrödinger equation and its solution for this case.

5.2. Do the same as in the preceeding problem for the three-dimensional case.

5.3. Find the relation between the wave functions $\psi'(x', t)$ and $\psi(x, t)$ that describe the motion of a non-relativistic particle in the inertial coordinate systems K' and K, given that the particle moves with a constant velocity v in the system K and that the system K' moves relative to K with a velocity v_0. For simplicity assume the velocities v and v_0 to have the same direction.

5.4. (a) Write down the Schrödinger equation for a particle in three dimensions moving under the action of a spherically symmetric elastic force, whose coefficient is k.

(b) Do the same for a charged particle moving in a Coulomb field.

5.5. Transform the Schrödinger equation in two dimensions from cartesian coordinates x, y to plane-polar coordinates r, φ.

5.6. What classes of solution of the Schrödinger equation are said to be stationary? Show that they arise only when the potential function U does not depend explicitly on time.

5.7. Why is it that when U does not depend explicitly on time the Schrödinger equation can be written in two forms:

$$\pm\, i\hbar\frac{\partial \Psi}{\partial t} = -\frac{\hbar^2}{2m}\varDelta\Psi + U\Psi,$$

i.e. with the plus or minus sign in front of the time derivative?[1]

5.8. Explain how the characteristic discreteness of eigenfunctions and of eigenvalues for parameters such as the energy of atomic systems follows from the Schrödinger equation.

5.9. Show that the energy of a freely moving particle can take any value (a continuous spectrum of eigenvalues E_n).

5.10. Consider the one-dimensional motion of a particle of mass m in a rectangular potential well of width l with absolutely impenetrable walls. Determine the eigenfunctions $\psi_n(x_2, t)$ and the eigenvalues of the energy parameter E_n. Investigate how, in solving the Schrödinger equation, the discreteness of the states of the particle arises.

5.11. Show that the eigenfunctions of the Schrödinger equation for a particle enclosed in a uniform rectangular potential well with infinitely high walls are orthogonal.

5.12. (a) Show, using the conditions of problem 5.10, that the number of nodes of any eigenfunction of a particle increases by one for each successive energy level.

(b) Calculate and draw to scale for the first three energy levels the probability distribution for finding the particle in problem 5.10 at any given point in space.

5.13. Prove by direct calculation that the average value of the x-coordinate of a particle enclosed in a uniform rectangular potential well with absolutely impenetrable walls is $l/2$, where l is the width of the potential well. Assume the origin of the coordinates to be at one of the walls of the well.

5.14. A particle of mass m can move only along a circle of radius r_0 in a potential independent of the azimuth angle φ.

(a) Find the possible values of the kinetic energy E and the angular momentum L for this particle.

(b) Find the eigenfunctions of the Schrödinger equation for the particle.

5.15. A particle moves in a two dimensional rectangular potential well with absolutely impenetrable walls (Fig. 7). The length of the edges of the well are equal to l_1 and l_2 respectively.

(a) Find the possible values of the energy of the particle.

(b) From the normalization condition find the expression for the wave functions of the particle.

(c) Find for example, for the state with quantum numbers $n_1 = 3$ and $n_2 = 2$, the coordinates of the points where the probability of finding the particle ia equal to zero and the coordinates of the points where this probability has maximum values.

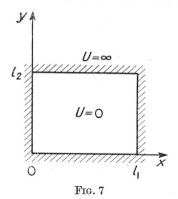

FIG. 7

5.16. Show that at the point where the value of potential energy of a particle undergoes a finite jump, the wave function remains "smooth", i.e. its first derivative is continuous. Prove this for the one dimensional case.

5.17. A particle of energy E moves in one dimension in a potential represented schematically in Fig. 8. Show that when $E < U_0$ the particle can assume any energy value E, i.e., its energy level spectrum is continuous.

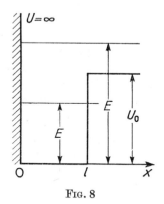

FIG. 8

5.18. A particle moves in the potential shown in Fig. 8 with a total energy $E > U_0$.

(a) Find the equation defining the possible energy values of the particle.

(b) Show by solving this equation graphically that the energy spectrum of the particle is discrete.

(c) Explain under what condition the particle can no longer be bound in the well.

5.19. A particle whose total energy is $E < U_0$ moves in the potential shown in Fig. 8.

(a) Indicate the region where the particle can be found. Explain why there exists a probability of finding the particle at points $x > l$ even for $E < U_0$.

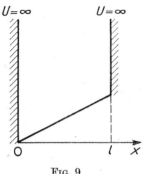

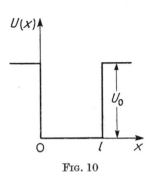

FIG. 9   FIG. 10

(b) Find how the probability density for the location of the particle depends upon the coordinate x and the difference $U_0 - E$.

(c) Find the ratio of the probabilities for finding the particle in the region to the right of the potential well and in the well itself.

5.20. Use the de Broglie concepts to make a qualitative sketch of the ψ-function of one of the excited states of a particle moving in a one-dimensional potential well (Fig. 9) with absolutely impenetrable walls.

5.21. A particle moves in the one-dimensional symmetrical potential well shown on Fig. 10.

(a) Derive an expression for all possible values of the total energy E in the range $E < U_0$.

(b) Show, by solving this equation graphically, that the energy spectrum of the particle is discrete.

5.22. From symmetry considerations it is evident that the probabilities of finding a particle to the left and to the right of the potential well shown on Fig. 10 should be equal, provided the total energy of the particle is $E < U_0$. Prove this by direct calculation.

5.23. Derive an equation giving the condtition that the probabilities of finding a particle of total energy E outside and inside the potential well shown on Fig. 10 are equal.

5.24. Find the equation that defines the possible energy values of a particle moving in the one-dimensional potential well (Fig. 11), assuming that its total energy E satisfies the following inequalities:

(a) $E < U_1$

(b) $U_1 < E < U_2$.

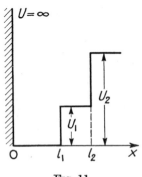

FIG. 11

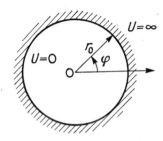

FIG. 12

5.25. A particle moves in a plane bounded by a circular cylindrical absolutely impenetrable wall (Fig. 12).

(a) Discuss the solution of the Schrödinger equation for this case.

(b) Show how the energy spectrum of the particle is necessarily discrete.

(c) Sketch graphically the approximate form of the curves on which the probability density for locating the particle is zero.

5.26. (a) Reduce the Schrödinger equation for a one-dimensional harmonic oscillator (a particle of mass m moving under an elastic force) to the form

$$\frac{d^2\psi}{d\xi^2} + (\lambda - \xi^2)\psi = 0$$

by introducing a new variable $\xi = \alpha x$. Find the values of the constants α and λ.

(b) Find an expression for the energy eigenvalues of the oscillator given that the physically admissible solutions of this equation exist only for the following values of the parameter λ:

$$\lambda = 2n + 1, \quad \text{where} \quad n = 0, 1, 2, \ldots$$

5.27. The general expression for the eigenfunctions of the Schrödinger equation for a harmonic oscillator (see the preceding problem) is of the form:[2]

$$\psi_n(\xi) = (-1)^n a_n e^{\xi^2/2} \frac{d^n}{d\xi^n} e^{-\xi^2},$$

here $\xi = ax$, and the a_n and α are constants.

(a) Find the eigenfunctions corresponding to the first three states ($n = 0, 1, 2$). Show that the number of nodes of ψ_n coincides with the value of n.

(b) Determine the shape of the probability distribution function for the particle in these states.

5.28. Show that the first two eigenfunctions of a harmonic oscillator are orthogonal.

5.29. Find the energy eigenvalues for the harmonic oscillator in the first two states ($n = 0, 1$) by directly substituting the corresponding eigenfunctions $\psi_0(x)$ and $\psi_1(x)$, taken from the answer to problem 5.27, into the Schrödinger equation:

$$\frac{d^2\psi}{d\xi^2} + (\lambda - \xi^2)\psi = 0$$

5.30 Use the results of problem 5.27 to find an expression for the normalization of the eigenfunctions $\psi_0(x)$ and $\psi_1(x)$ of a harmonic oscillator in its first two states ($n = 0, 1$).

Hint: Use the values of the integrals given in Appendix 6.

5.31. Use the expressions for the normalization of the eigenfunctions of a harmonic oscillator (see the solution of problem 5.30) to calculate the values of $\overline{x}$ and $\overline{x^2}$:

(a) for the ground state ($n = 0$),

(b) for the state with $n = 1$.

5.32. The wave function of the ground state of a particle moving under the action of an elastic force is of the form

$$\psi_0(x) = a e^{-ax^2/2},$$

where

$$a = \sqrt[4]{mk/\hbar^2},$$

m is the mass of the particle and k the elastic force modulus.

Calculate for this state the probability of finding the particle outside the limits permitted by classical mechanics.

Hint: Use the numerical values of the integrals given in Appendix 6.

5.33. In quantum mechanics it is proved that the square of the operator representing the angular momentum has eigenvalues $L^2 = \hbar^2 \lambda$ where λ is the eigenvalue determining the function $Y(\vartheta, \varphi)$ in the equation

$$\frac{1}{\sin\vartheta}\frac{\partial}{\partial\vartheta}\left(\sin\vartheta\frac{\partial}{\partial}\frac{Y}{\vartheta}\right) + \frac{1}{\sin^2\vartheta}\frac{\partial^2 Y}{\partial\varphi^2} + \lambda Y = 0.$$

It is also known that the product

$$u = r^l Y(\vartheta, \varphi),$$

where $l = 0, 1, 2 \ldots$ satisfies the Laplace equation $\nabla^2 U = 0$. Find from this the possible values of the parameter λ and of the square of the angular momentum, L^2.

5.34. Find the form of the (three-dimensional) spherically symmetric wave functions $\psi(r)$. For a particle, moving in a spherically symmetrical potential well with absolutely impenetrable walls: $U(r) = 0$ for $r < r_0$ and $U(r) = \infty$ for $r \geq r_0$. Determine also the corresponding energy eigenvalues of the particle.

Hint: Use the substitution $x(r) = r\psi(r)$.

5.35. A particle moves in the spherically symmetrical potential well shown in Fig. 13. Show that when the energy of the particle is $E < U_0$ its energy spectrum will be discrete. Consider only the

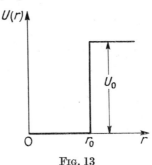

FIG. 13

spherically symmetrical states of the particle, i.e., those in which its wave function is $\psi(r)$, a function of r only.

Hint: Use the substitution $x(r) = r\psi(r)$.

5.36. (a) Write out the Schrödinger equation in spherical co-ordinates for an electron moving in the Coloumb field of a fixed nucleus with charge Ze (a hydrogen-like system).

(b) Separate the equation into its radial and angular parts.

(c) Find the explicit dependence of the wave function on the azimuth angle φ.

5.37. The radial part of the Schrödinger equation for an electron in the field of a nucleus Z is of the form:

$$\frac{1}{r^2} \frac{d}{dr} \left(r^2 \frac{dR}{dr} \right) + \left[\frac{2m}{\hbar^2} \left(E + \frac{Ze^2}{r} \right) - \frac{\lambda}{r^2} \right] R = 0 .$$

(a) Find the asymptotic form of the radial part of the wave function, $R(r)$, for large values of the radius r. Consider the two cases $E > 0$ and $E < 0$.

(b) From the fact that the parameter $\lambda = l(l + 1)$, where l is the orbital quantum number ($l = 0, 1, 2, ...$), determine the form of the function $R(r)$ for small distances from the nucleus.

Hint: In both cases use the substitution $x(r) = rR(r)$.

5.38. Determine the eigenenergy E_1 of the hydrogen atom in the $1s$-state, for which the eigenfunction is spherically sym-metrical: $\psi(r) = a e^{-\alpha r}$.

Here a and α are constants.

5.39. The eigenfunction of the $1s$-state of the hydrogen atom is of the form

$$\psi(r) = a e^{-r/r_1}$$

where r_1 is the first Bohr radius.

(a) Determine the probability in this state of finding an electron at a distance between r and $r + dr$ from the nucleus.

(b) At what distance from the nucleus will the probability of finding the electron be greatest?

(c) Draw the approximate form of $\psi(r)$ and of the probability $W(r)$.

5.40. Calculate the distances at which the radial component of the probability of finding the electron in a hydrogen atom is maximum for the $2p$ and $3d$ states, given that the radial parts of the wave functions in these states are respectively:

$$R_{2p}(r) = a_2 r e^{-r/2r_1} \quad \text{and} \quad R_{3d}(r) = a_3 r^2 e^{-r/3r_1},$$

where r_1 is the first Bohr radius.

5.41. Give the spectral notation for the states of a hydrogen atom whose energy levels respectively 4- and 9-fold degenerate. Determine also the energies of these states.

5.42. Write down the Schrödinger equation for a helium atom.

5.43. Write down the wave equation for the electrons in a hydrogen molecule.

5.44. Find the reflection coefficient R and the transparency D of the potential barrier represented in Fig. 14 for a particle in one dimension moving from left to right with energy E, assuming $E > U_0$.

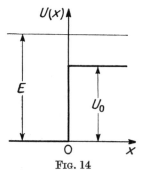

FIG. 14

5.45. Show that the transparency coefficient of the potential barrier represented in Fig. 15 is zero for a particle with an energy $E < U_0$.

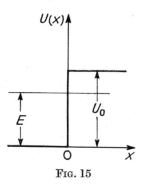

FIG. 15

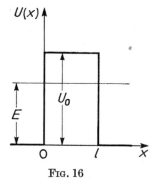

FIG. 16

5.46. Find an expression for the probability that a particle of energy E will pass through the rectangular potential barrier shown in Fig. 16. Consider the case $E < U_0$.

5.47. The probability that a particle of energy E will leak through a rectangular barrier of height U_0 is given by the transparency coefficient D, which, for $E < U_0$, takes on the form

$$D = A e^{-\frac{2}{\hbar} \sqrt{2m(U_0 - E)}\, l}.$$

Here A is a constant of the order of 1, m the mass of the particle and l the potential barrier width.

Calculate and represent graphically how D depends upon the barrier width l for an electron, when the difference $U_0 - E$ is:

(a) 1 eV,

(b) 5 eV.

5.48. The probability that a particle of energy E will pass through a potential barrier of arbitrary shape is described sufficiently accurately by the following expression:[4]

$$D = A e^{-\frac{2}{\hbar} \int_{x_1}^{x_2} \sqrt{2m(U - E)}\, dx}.$$

Here A is a constant of the order of 1, m the mass of the particle, x_1 and x_2 the coordinates of the points between which the potential energy U is greater than E.

Putting $A = 1$, estimate the value of D for an electron in the case of the potential barrier shown in Fig. 17 for two values of the electric field strength to the right of the point $x = 0$: $E_1 = 10^7$ V/cm and $E_2 = 2 \times 10^7$ V/cm, assuming $U_0 - E = 1$ eV.

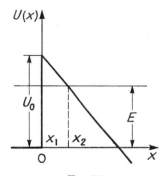

FIG. 17

REFERENCES

1. L. D. LANDAU and I. M. LIFSHITZ, *Quantum Mechanics*, English translation, Pergamon Press, 1958, p. 52.
2. *op. cit.*, p. 67.
3. *op. cit.*, p. 126.
4. *op. cit.*, Chapter VII.

6. SPECTRA OF THE ALKALI METALS.

FINE STRUCTURE

1. The spectral terms[1] of alkali metal atoms are given by the expression:

$$T = \frac{R Z_{eff}^2}{(n + \sigma_l)^2} \ \text{cm}^{-1},$$

where

$Z_{eff} = 1$ for the atoms of alkali metal;

$\qquad$ 2, 3, ... for the isoelectronic series of alkali-like ions.

Here R is Rydberg's constant, n the principal quantum number, and σ_l the Rydberg constant correction, which depends on the orbital quantum number l.

2. The term diagram typical of alkali metal atoms is shown on Fig. 18. The diagram shows the transitions that give rise to the main spectral series: principal, sharp, diffuse and fundamental.

3. The resonance spectral line corresponds to the transition of an atom from a first excited state to the ground state. This line defines the first excitation potential.

4. The Dirac expression for the fine structure of hydrogen-like ions is

$$T = \frac{R Z^2}{n^2} + \frac{\alpha^2 R Z^4}{n^3} \left(\frac{1}{j + \dfrac{1}{2}} - \frac{3}{4n} \right).$$

Here Z is the atomic number of the nucleus,

$\qquad R$ Rydberg's constant,

$\qquad \alpha$ the fine structure constant,

$\qquad n$ the principal quantum number,

$\qquad j$ the intrinsic quantum number, which describes the total angular momentum of the electron.

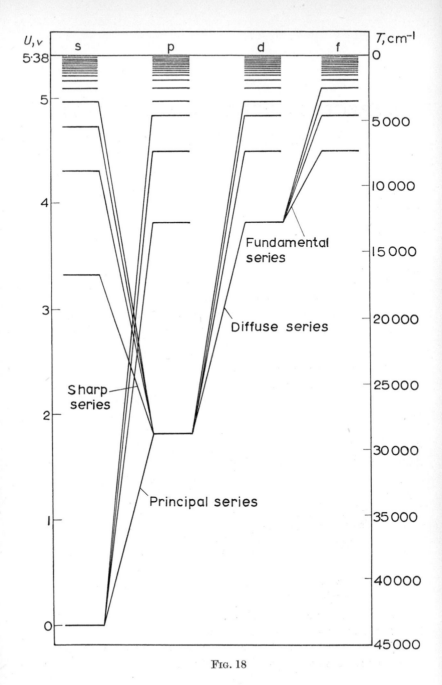

FIG. 18

5. The expression for the decrease in time of the number of excited atoms is given by:

$$N = N_0 e^{-\frac{t}{\tau}},$$

where N_0 is the number of atoms initially excited, and τ the mean life-time of an atom in an excited state.

6. The uncertainty relation for energy connects the width Γ of an energy level and the time τ spent in a given state:

$$\Gamma \tau \cong \hbar,$$

where $\hbar$ is Planck's constant, 1.05×10^{-27} erg. sec.

7. The number of excited atoms in a state of energy E in a gas at thermodynamic equilibrium at temperature T, is given by

$$N = \frac{g}{g_0} N_0 e^{-\frac{E - E_0}{kT}},$$

where N_o is the number of atoms in a state of energy E_0 and g/g_0 the ratio of the statistical weights of the corresponding states.

Spectra of the Alkali Metals

6.1. Calculate the terms for the ground levels of the alkali atoms whose ionization potentials are as follows: lithium 5·38 V; sodium 5·14 V; potassium 4·33 V; rubidium 4·17 V and caesium 3·89 V. Calculate also the short wave limits of the principal series of these elements.

6.2. The table below gives the values of the spectral terms (in cm^{-1}) for the lithium atom:

n	s	p	d	f
2	43,486	28,582	–	–
3	16,280	12,560	12,203	–
4	8475	7018	6864	6856
5	–	–	4390	4382

(a) Calculate the Rydberg constant corrections for these terms and show that the corrections are constant within each series of terms.

(b) Show which terms are the most hydrogen-like in behaviour and give an explanation for this.

6.3. The fundamental term of the lithium atom is T_{2s} = 43,486 cm^{-1}. What spectral lines arise when an excited atom returns from the state $3p$ to the state $2s$, given that the 3233 Å line corresponds to the direct transition $3p \to 2s$?

6.4. Calculate and construct to scale a term diagram for the sodium atom, whose ground state is $3s$. The wavelengths of the resonance line (589 mμ), of the principal line of the diffuse series (819 mμ) and of the principal line of the fundamental series (1846 mμ) and the limit of the principal series (241·3 mμ) are given. Restrict yourself to the terms whose principal quantum numbers n are 3 and 4.

6.5. Find the wavelengths of the spectral lines arising in the transition of excited sodium atoms from the $4s$ state to the $3s$ ground state. Assume that the Rydberg corrections for the s and p terms are respectively equal to $-1·37$ and $-0·9$.

6.6. The wavelength of the resonance line of potassium, which corresponds to the transition $4p \to 4s$, is 7665 Å, and the wavelength of the principal series limit is 2858 Å. Hence determine the Rydberg corrections for the s and p terms of the potassium atom.

6.7. The Rydberg corrections for the S, P and D terms of the sodium atom are respectively equal to: $-1·37$, $-0·9$ and $-0·01$. Representing the terms by the expression

$$R(z - a)^2/n^2,$$

where Z is the atomic number of the nucleus, calculate the corrections a for the terms $3s$, $3p$ and $3d$. What is the physical meaning of the correction a?

6.8. The ionization potentials of the terms of an isoelectronic series are as follows: Li (5·38 V), Be$^+$ (17·0 V) and B^{++} (35·6 V).

(a) Using these data draw the graph of the function

$$\sqrt{T}/R = f(Z),$$

where T is the value of the term that corresponds to the ground state, R is Rydberg's constant and Z the atomic number.

(b) Determine from the graph the values of the principal quantum numbers and the magnitudes of the screening corrections (Rydberg's constant corrections) for the ground states of Li, Be$^+$ and B^{++}.

FINE STRUCTURE AND NATURAL WIDTH
OF SPECTRAL LINES

6.9. What experimental facts show that an electron has an intrinsic angular momentum and a magnetic moment?

6.10. Describe briefly the following gyromagnetic experiments: magnetization by rotation (Barnett effect), rotation by magnetization (Einstein–de Haas effect).[2] What is the significance of these experiments?

6.11. From Bohr's theory of the atom estimate the order of magnitude of the maximum energy of magnetic interaction between the spin and the orbit of the electron in a hydrogen atom in its ground state. (Assume the orbital magnetic field can be represented by a dipole.)

6.12. Show in general that the correction term in the fine structure formula does not vanish for any possible values of the quantum numbers n and j.

6.13. From the solutions of Schrödinger's equation for the hydrogen atom and the alkali metal atoms one obtains directly the principal and the orbital quantum numbers. Why does this equation not give the spin quantum number?

6.14. Calculate in wavelengths the interval between the components of the doublet corresponding to the transition $2p - 1s$ in the hydrogen atom.

6.15. Set up the term scheme for the singly ionized helium atom in a state whose principal quantum number is $n = 3$. Express the intervals between the terms on the energy and the wave number scales.

6.16. Set up the scheme of allowed transitions between the states with principal quantum numbers $n = 4$ and $n = 3$ for the singly ionized helium atom. The selection rules for l and j are: $\Delta l = \pm 1$; $\Delta j = 0, \pm 1$. Determine the difference in wave numbers between the extreme components of the multiplet.

6.17. It is known that in contrast to the other terms, s terms are always singlets.

(a) Can this be seen from the fine structure formula?

(b) What is the physical meaning of this?

6.18. It follows from an analysis of the fine structure of alkali metal spectra that their terms are doublets, except for the s terms, which are singlets. Could one conclude that only the s terms are singlets from the fact that the magnitude of the splitting (in wave numbers) for all the spectral lines of the sharp series is the same, while for the lines of the principal series it is not?

6.19. Calculate what fraction of atoms will remain in an excited state during an interval of time equal to their mean lifetime in this state.

6.20. A closed vessel of volume $V = 100 \text{ cm}^3$ is filled with lithium gas at a temperature $T = 1500°\text{K}$ and a pressure of 0.1 mm Hg. The total radiative emissive power of the resonance line of wavelength 7608 Å amounts to $W = 1.74$ W. Determine the mean lifetime of lithium atoms in the resonance excited state.

6.21. One method for determining the mean life of atoms in an excited state consists in observing the decrease in the intensity of luminescence along an atomic beam in a high vacuum. Calculate the value τ for those atoms in a state of resonance excitation, given that the emission intensity of the resonance line along the beam drops by a factor of 3.32 along a distance of 1.5 mm, the velocity of the atoms in the beam being 10^5 cm/sec.

6.22. Give the fundamental factors that determine the width of spectral lines.

6.23. It is known that the resonance line of mercury $(\lambda = 2537 \text{ Å})$ arises in the transition of the atoms from an excited state to the ground state, the mean lifetime in the former state being $\tau = 10^{-7}$ sec. Determine the ratio of the Doppler broadening of this line at room temperature to its natural width.[3]

6.24. To obtain spectral lines without Doppler broadening one uses a method based on the observation of the fluorescence of excited atoms in a narrow, slightly divergent beam of canal rays. The observation is made in a direction strictly perpendicular to the beam. Determine the necessary aperture angle of a beam of sodium atoms for which the Doppler broadening of the resonance line (5896 Å) is equal to $\eta = 10$ per cent of its natural width. Assume that the lifetime of the sodium atom in the state of resonance excitation is $\tau = 1.6 \times 10^{-8}$ sec and that the velocity of the atoms in the beam is $v = 10^5$ cm/sec.

6.25. Atomic hydrogen is at a temperature of 10,000°K. Determine the ratio of numbers of atoms excited to the second and the third energy levels ($n = 2$ and $n = 3$), assuming that the statistical weights of these states are equal to their degrees of degeneracy.

6.26. Estimate the temperature of a gas consisting of caesium atoms, given that the intensities of the components of a doublet resonance line (whose wavelengths are 8943·5 and 8521·1 Å) are in the ratio 2 : 3.

6.27. In the case of thermal radiation the intensity ratio of the components of narrow multiplets can be determined sufficiently accurately using only the degree of degeneracy of the corresponding energy sublevels.

(a) Using this, find the intensity ratio of the components of the narrow doublets of the principal series of alkali metals.

(b) Estimate the error resulting from this approximation due to the unequal populations of the doublet levels for the intensity ratio of the components of the sodium (5890 and 5896 Å) and potassium (7645 and 7699 Å) doublets, both at a temperature of 2000°K.

REFERENCES

1. cf., for instance, H. G. KUHN, *Atomic Spectra*, Longmans, 1962.

2. L. F. BATES, *Modern Magnetism*, Cambridge University Press, Chapter VII.

3. F. K. RICHTMEYER and E. H. KENNARD, *Introduction to Modern Physics*, McGraw-Hill, 4th Edition (1956), p. 397.

7. THE ATOM IN A MAGNETIC FIELD

1. The values corresponding to the classical angular momentum of an electron and of the electron shell of an atom (orbital p_L, spin p_S and total p_J) are given by the expressions:

$$p_L = \hbar \sqrt{L(L + 1)},$$
$$p_S = \hbar \sqrt{S(S + 1)},$$
$$p_J = \hbar \sqrt{J(J + 1)},$$

where L, S and J are respectively the orbital, the spin and the intrinsic quantum numbers; $\hbar$ is Planck's constant.

2. The expression for μ, the effective magnetic moment of the atom, and its projection on an external magnetic field μ_H is:

$$\mu = g\mu_0 \sqrt{J(J + 1)},$$
$$\mu_H = g\,\mu_0 m_J,$$

where g is the Landé factor (see 3 below);
μ_0 the Bohr magneton,
J the intrinsic quantum number,
m_j the magnetic quantum number.

3. The Landé splitting factor is

$$g = 1 + \frac{J(J + 1) + S(S + 1) - L(L + 1)}{2J(J + 1)},$$

where L, S and J are the orbital, spin and intrinsic quantum numbers respectively.

A similar expression is valid also for the individual electron, i.e. for the quantum numbers l, s and j.

4. The energy of an atom in an external magnetic field is

$$E_H = E_0 - \mu_H H,$$

where μ_H is the projection of the magnetic moment of the atom on the direction of the field H;

E_0 is the energy of the atom in the absence of the magnetic field, more precisely when $\mu \perp \mathbf{H}$.

5. The frequency of the Larmor precession of the electron shell of an atom in an external magnetic field H is:

$$\omega_L = g\,\frac{eH}{2\,mc}\ \text{rad/sec},$$

where g is the Landé factor (the gyromagnetic ratio); e and m are the charge and the mass of the electron; c is the velocity of light.

6. The expression for the splitting of spectral lines in the normal Zeeman effect is

$$\Delta\bar{\nu} = \frac{eH}{4\pi mc^2}\ [\text{cm}^{-1}].$$

7. The expression for the splitting of spectral lines in the anomalous Zeeman effect is:

$$\Delta\bar{\nu} = (m_1 g_1 - m_2 g_2)\,\frac{eH}{4\pi mc^2}\ \text{cm}^{-1},$$

where m_1 and m_2 are the magnetic quantum numbers of the terms between which the transition takes place, and g_1 and g_2 are the corresponding Landé factors.

8. The selection rules for the quantum numbers defining the allowed transitions in atoms are:

$$\Delta S = 0 \qquad\qquad \Delta m_S = 0$$

$$\Delta L = \pm 1 \qquad\qquad \Delta m_L = 0, \pm 1$$

$$\Delta J = 0, \pm 1 \qquad\qquad \Delta m_J = 0, \pm 1$$

$$J = 0 \not\rightarrow J = 0 \qquad\qquad m_J = 0 \not\rightarrow m_J = 0$$

VECTOR MODEL OF THE ATOM

7.1. In an excited helium atom one of the electrons is in a p state and the other in a d state. Find the possible values of the total orbital quantum number L and of the quasi-classical angular momentum corresponding to it.

ANP 3

7.2. Determine the angle between the orbital angular momenta of two electrons, one of which is in a d state, the other in an f state, assuming that:

(a) the total orbital quantum number is $L = 3$;

(b) the unknown angle is the minimum possible;

(c) the unknown angle is the maximum possible.

7.3. What are the possible values of the total angular momentum of an electron in a d state? What are the angles between the spin and the orbital angular momentum?

7.4. Determine the possible values of the quantum number J corresponding to the angular momentum of an electron system with $L = 3$, when S has the following values: $3/2$, 2, $5/2$, 4.

7.5. When $L > S$ the number of possible states is $2S + 1$, and when $L < S$ it is $2L + 1$. Show this, by writing down explicitly all possible values of the quantum number J for the following cases:

(a) $L = 3,\ S = 2$ (c) $L = 3,\ S = 7/2$

(b) $L = 2,\ S = 3/2$ (d) $L = 2,\ S = 3$

Give an expression for all possible values of J when $L = S$.

7.6. The multiplicity of the term symbols is denoted by the number $2S + 1$ even when $S > L$, that is, when it no longer determines the number of possible values of J. What is the meaning of such a symbolism?

7.7. On the basis of the vector model of the atom explain how is it that there are two systems of terms (singlets and triplets) for atoms with two valence electrons.

7.8. Show on the example of the two electron system ($l_1 = 2, l_2 = 3$) that both types of coupling (Russell–Saunders (or $L - S$) coupling and $j - j$ coupling) give the same number of possible states. Will the difference between the two types of coupling manifest itself in any way?

7.9. Write out all the possible terms for a combination of a p-electron and a d-electron using Russell–Saunders coupling. Give their spectral notations.

7.10. The photon emitted by an excited atom carries with it a certain angular momentum. How can this be reconciled with the fact that the selection rules for the intrinsic quantum number valid for radiating atoms allow the possibility that, in addition to $\Delta J = \pm 1$, $\Delta J = 0$ may also occur.

7.11. A hydrogen atom is in a ^1F-state. Find the magnitude of the corresponding orbital magnetic moment and the possible values of its projection on the direction of the external magnetic field.

7.12. Determine the magnitude of the greatest possible additional energy acquired by the orbital magnetic moment of an atom in a ^1D state in magnetic fields of 10,000 and 500,000 oe.

7.13. Calculate the Landé splitting factors for atoms with one valence electron in S, P and D states.

7.14. Calculate the Landé factors for atoms in the state ^3P (the triplet term). Show also, that for all S-states (except the singlet) $g = 2$.

7.15. Using the vector model of the atom, compare the magnitude of the total magnetic moment in the $^3P_2$ state with the magnitude of the effective magnetic moment in the same state.

7.16. Show that the terms $^4D_{1/2}$ and $^6G_{3/2}$ do not split in a magnetic field. Interpret this fact from the point of view of the vector model of the atom.

7.17. Derive an expression for the frequency of the Larmor precession of the electron shell of an atomic without spin in an external magnetic field, starting from the relation

$$\frac{d\mathbf{P}}{dt} = \mathbf{M},$$

where $\mathbf{P}$ is the angular momentum of the system and $\mathbf{M}$ the moment of the forces acting.

7.18. Calculate the frequencies of the Larmor precessions of the electronic shells of atoms for which the spin is zero:

(a) in the magnetic field of the earth ($H \approx 0.5$ oe),
(b) in a magnetic field of 500,000 oe.

Compare the results obtained with the frequency of revolution of an electron in the first Bohr orbit of a hydrogen atom.

7.19. Find the angular velocities of precession of atoms in the states ^1P, $^2S_{1/2}$ and $^2P_{3/2}$ in a magnetic field $H = 100$ oe.

7.20. A nickel atom in its ^3F ground state in a magnetic field of strength $H = 500$ oe. The angular frequency of precession of

3*

the atom is then $5 \cdot 5 \times 10^9$ rad/sec. Determine the minimum additional energy acquired by the atom in this field.

ZEEMAN EFFECT. THE STERN–GERLACH EXPERIMENT

7.21. For which spectral lines does the normal Zeeman effect occur? Give the spectral notation for the two terms (with $L = 2$ and 3), between which a transition corresponds to such a line.

7.22. Construct the scheme of transitions that take place in a between which a transition corresponds a magnetic field between the following singlet states:

(a) $L = 2 \rightarrow L = 1$,

(b) $F \rightarrow D$.

Show that all possible transitions give only three lines in either case.

7.23. Explain qualitatively from a classical point of view the difference in the nature of the line splitting observed in directions perpendicular and parallel to the magnetic field.

7.24. Find the total splitting (in electron volts and wave numbers) of the term ^1D in a magnetic field of 50,000 oe.

7.25. Give the spectral notation of the singlet term for which the total splitting increases by $\Delta T = 1 \cdot 4$ cm^{-1}, if the magnetic field is increased by $\Delta H = 5000$ oe.

7.26. Determine the resolving power and the number of lines of a diffraction grating capable of resolving the components of a spectral line of wavelength 5365 Å in second order, when the normal Zeeman effect is observed in the direction of the magnetic field. The field strength is $H = 2000$ oe.

7.27. How can one explain the fact that the normal Zeeman effect can be interpreted from the point of view of both classical and quantum theory (with the vector model of the atom)?

7.28. How does the anomalous Zeeman effect differ from the normal one? Which effect will be shown in a weak magnetic field by the spectral lines of the following atomic gases: H, He, Li, Be, B and C?

7.29. Which effect (the normal or the anomalous) will be shown in a weak magnetic field by the lines resulting from the transitions between the following terms:

$$1_{P_1} - 1_{S_0}; \quad 2_{D_{5/2}} - 2_{P_{3/2}}; \quad 3_{F_4} - 3_{D_3}?$$

7.30. In the anomalous Zeeman effect a magnetic field is considered "strong" if the magnitude of the Zeeman splitting is comparable to the natural multiplet splitting.

(a) Compare the magnitude of the natural splitting of the lithium ^2P state with the interval between neighbouring levels of the term $^2P_{3/2}$ in Zeeman splitting in a magnetic field of $H = 5000$ oe.

(b) Will a field of 50,000 oe be "strong" in this case?

Hint: Estimate the magnitude of the natural multiplet splitting from the interaction of a spin and an orbital magnetic moment, assuming that their distance is of the order of 10^{-8} cm.

7.31. A spectral line arises as the result of the transition $^2P_{3/2} \rightarrow {}^2S_{1/2}$.

(a) Into how many components will this line split in a "weak" magnetic field?

(b) Determine in wave numbers the total splitting of this line in a weak magnetic field of $H = 1000$ oe.

7.32. The wavelengths of the sodium doublet that arises in the $3P \rightarrow 3S$ transition are 5895·3 and 5889·96 Å. Hence find the magnitude of the magnetic field strength for which the lowest sublevel of the $^2P_{3/2}$ term will coincide with the upper sublevel of the $^2P_{1/2}$ term.

7.33. What quantum numbers describe the state of an electron in an atom in the cases of a "weak" and of a "strong" magnetic field?

7.34. Represent on an energy diagram the splitting of the terms in a "weak" and a "strong" magnetic field for ^2S and ^2P states. Show the possible transitions and determine the number of spectral lines in the two cases.

7.35. How does one explain the fact that in the Paschen–Back effect, contrary to the normal Zeeman effect, each component of a triplet has a fine structure; e.g., for atoms with one valence electron a doublet structure?

7.36. (a) Atoms with an intrinsic magnetic moment move transversely to

1. a uniform,

2. a non-uniform

magnetic field. What is the difference in their behaviour?

(b) Atoms with a positive projection of magnetic moment on the direction of the external field vector move in a transverse non-uniform magnetic field. In what direction relative to the field will they deviate?

7.37. (a) Why is it that in order to observe the spin-$1/2$ character of the electron in the Stern–Gerlach experiments one must use beams of atoms all in the ground state and belonging to the first group of the periodic system?

(b) Why is it that in this experiment the spin of the nucleus does not interfere with the observation of the spin of the electron?

7.38. In the Stern–Gerlach experiment a narrow beam of silver atoms, all in their ground states, is allowed to pass in a direction perpendicular to a strong non-uniform magnetic field with a gradient $\partial H/\partial z = 10^5$ oe/cm. The extension of the magnetic field is $l_1 = 4$ cm and the distance between the magnet and the screen is $l_2 = 10$ cm (see Fig. 19). Determine the value of the projection of the electronic magnetic moment μ_H on the direction of the magnetic field, assuming that the magnitude of the beam splitting on the screen amounts to $\Delta l = 2$ mm and the velocity of the atoms is $v = 5 \times 10^4$ cm/sec.

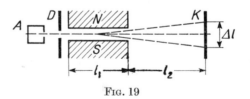

FIG. 19

7.39. When a narrow beam of caesium atoms in the ground state passes through a strong perpendicular non-uniform magnetic field, 5 cm in extent, a splitting of the beam is observed on a screen at 10 cm from the magnet (Fig. 19). Determine the force acting on the caesium atoms in the magnetic field, if the splitting amounts to 2·5 mm and the kinetic energy of the atoms in the beam is equal to the mean thermal energy at a temperature of $T = 10^3 °$K.

7.40. Determine the maximum values of the projections of the magnetic moments of vanadium (^4F), manganese (^6S) and iron (^5D) atoms, given that beams of such atoms, where passing through a strong non-uniform magnetic field, as in the Stern–Gerlach experiment, are split respectively into 4, 6, and 9 components. The above data in brackets give the states of the atoms.

7.41. In one of the experiments on the splitting of atomic beams in a strong non-uniform magnetic field according to the Stern–Gerlach method, atoms of vanadium in the $^4F_{3/2}$ ground state were used. The velocity of the atoms is 400 m/sec. Find the distance between the extreme components of the beam on a screen, if the parameters of the experimental arrangement are (Fig. 19): $l_1 = 3$ cm, $l_2 = 10$ cm, $\partial H/\partial z = 10^{-5}$ oe/cm.

7.42. What happens to a beam of atoms with an intrinsic magnetic moment μ as it passes through a system of two successive strongly non-uniform magnetic fields, each of which is perpendicular to the other and to the beam direction?

8. DIAMAGNETISM AND PARAMAGNETISM

1. The magnetization per unit volume I_0 of a diamagnetic substance is

$$I_0 = \chi B, \quad \chi = -\frac{N_0 Z e^2}{6 m c^2} \overline{r^2},$$

where:

χ is the diamagnetic susceptibility per unit volume of the substance,

B the magnetic induction,

N_0 the number of atoms per unit volume,

Z the atomic number,

e and m the charge and mass of the electron respectively,

c the velocity of light and

$\overline{r^2}$ the mean square distance of the electrons from the nucleus.

2. The magnetization per unit volume I_0 of a paramagnetic substance is (Langevin's formula):

$$I_0 = N_0 \mu \left(\cot a - \frac{1}{a} \right), \quad a = \frac{\mu H}{k T},$$

where

N_0 is the number of atoms (or molecules) per unit volume,

μ the magnetic moment of an atom (a molecule),

H the magnetic field strength,

k the Boltzmann constant and

T the absolute temperature.

(a) The case of a "weak" magnetic field is described by

$$I_0 = \chi B, \quad \chi = \frac{N_0 \mu^2}{3 k} \frac{1}{T},$$

where $N_0 \mu^2 / 3k$ is the Curie constant per unit volume of the substance;

(b) The "strong" magnetic field case is given by:

$$I = N_0 \mu.$$

3. The magnetization per unit volume I_0 of a paramagnetic substance in a "weak" magnetic field, taking into account quantization of the atomic moments, is:

$$I_0 = \frac{N_0 \mu_0^2 g^2 j(j+1)}{3kT} B,$$

where μ_0 is the Bohr magneton,
  g the Landé factor,
  j the intrinsic quantum number of an atom.

8.1. Show that the magnetic moment of an atom due to the Larmor precession of the electron shell in an external magnetic always has opposite direction to the magnetic field.

8.2. (a) Consider a series of atomic gases:

$$\text{He } (^2S_0), \quad \text{Li } (^2S_{1/2}), \quad \text{Be } (^1S_0), \quad \text{C } (^1P_0),$$
$$\text{V } (^4F_{3/2}) \quad \text{and} \quad \text{Mn } (^6S_{5/2})$$

(the states of the atoms are given in brackets). Which of the listed gases will be diamagnetic and which paramagnetic?

(b) How can one explain the fact that, for example, copper and bismuth, whose atoms in the gaseous state correspond to the terms $^2S_{1/2}$ and $^2S_{3/2}$ respectively, are diamagnetic when in the solid state?

8.3. Estimate the magnitude of the diamagnetic susceptibility of one mole of helium, assuming that the diameters of the atoms' are of the order of 1 Å.

8.4. It is known that the values of the magnetic permeability of such diamagnetics as copper and bismuth (in the solid state) differ from 1 by $8 \cdot 8 \times 10^{-6}$ and 176×10^{-6} respectively. Determine the values of the average magnetic moments per atom of each of these substances in a magnetic field of strength 1000 oe.

8.5. A gas consisting of hydrogen atoms is placed in a magnetic field of $H = 2000$ oe. Using the Bohr model of the atom, in which the magnetic moment is caused by the orbital motion of the electron, find the mean value of the induced magnetic moment of the atom $\Delta\mu$ that arises as a result of the Larmor precession of the electronic shells in the external field. Assume that the electrons in the atoms are in the first Bohr orbit and that the distribution of orientations of the orbits is uniform in all directions.

8.6. The magnetic moment of one mole of a certain paramagnetic gas at a temperature of 300°K proves to be 0·15 erg/gauss when a magnetic field of 100 oe is switched on. From these data determine the Curie constant per mole and the magnitude of the magnetic moment of a molecule.

8.7. Calculate the magnetic moment of a molecule of nitrogen, given that at room temperature the magnetic moment of one mole of the gas in a weak field $H = 100$ oe is $I = 2\cdot11 \times 10^{-3}$ erg/gauss.

8.8. Find by how much the magnetic permeability of a paramagnetic gas differs from 1 given that the gas is at n.t.p. and that the magnetic moment of each molecule is equal to 2·5 Bohr magnetons.

8.9. (a) Calculate the magnetization of 1 cm³ of oxygen at n.t.p. in a "strong" and in a "weak" ($H = 100$ oe) magnetic field. The magnetic moment of the oxygen molecule is equal to $2\cdot6 \times 10^{-20}$ erg/gauss.

(b) Compare this with the magnetization of 1 cm³ of copper (which is diamagnetic) in a magnetic field of 50 koe. Assume that the mean square distance of the electrons from the nucleus is $6\cdot1 \times 10^{-18}$ cm.

8.10. A gas at 100°K consists of molecules with a magnetic moment of 2·5 Bohr magnetons; the gas is in an external magnetic field of 200 koe. Determine by how many percent the magnetic moment of the gas under these conditions differs from its magnitude at total saturation.

8.11. Assume that the distribution in energy of magnetic moments of molecules in an external magnetic field H is according to Boltzmann's law and find the general expression for the mean projection of the magnetic dipole on the external field at temperature T. The magnetic moment of each molecule is μ.

8.12. The general expression for the average component of magnetic moment of a molecule in an external field is:

$$\bar{\mu}_H = \mu \left(\cot a - \frac{1}{a} \right),$$

where μ is the magnetic moment of a molecule and $a = \mu H/kT$.

(a) Simplify this expression for the cases of a "weak" and of a "strong" magnetic field H.

(b) Calculate the magnitude of the average component of magnetic moment of a molecule in the direction of an external field of 10 and of 500 koe. The gas is at room temperature and the magnetic moment of a molecule is 1 Bohr magneton.

8.13. What is the force acting on 1 cm^3 of a certain paramagnetic gas located in a non-uniform magnetic field under the following hypothetical conditions: the strength and the gradient of the field are $H = 300$ koe and $\partial H/\partial x = 360$ oe/cm respectively, the gas temperature is $-236°C$, the magnetic moment of a molecule is $\mu = 5\cdot5$ Bohr magnetons. The pressure is normal.

8.14. Draw the graph of the Langevin function. What is its physical significance? Determine from the curve the values of the magnetic field strengths for which the corresponding points of the Langevin curve will differ from the asymptote by 50 and by 10 per cent. Make the calculation for a gas at room temperature consisting of molecules whose magnetic monent is 1 Bohr magneton.

8.15. Derive the general expression (3), above, for the average component of magnetic moment of gas molecules in a "weak" magnetic field H, starting from the following assumptions:

(a) Only such directions of magnetic moment are possible for which the component in the direction of the external field satisfies the conditions of quantization of angular momentum.

(b) The energy distribution of molecules in an external magnetic field follows Boltzmann's law.

8.16. A gas consisting of atoms of a certain alkali metal in its graund state is placed in a magnetic field of $H = 30$ koe. Calculate the ratio between the number of atoms with a positive component of magnetic moment in the direction of the external field to the number of atoms with a negative component. The gas is at room temperature.

8.17. A gas of lithium atoms in the ground state is in a magnetic field of 1000 oe. Calculate the magnetization of 1 g of this gas at room temperature.

8.18. Calculate from the quantum mechanical formula the value of the paramagnetic susceptibility of 1 g of atomic hydrogen in a "weak" field. The gas is at room temperature and its atoms are in the ground state.

8.19. One gram of a gas consists of a mixture of atoms of vanadium ($^4F_{3/2}$) and iron ($^5D_4$) in a proportion by weight of $4:1$ (the ground states of the atoms are given in brackets). Find the magnetic moment of this mass of gas, when it is in a magnetic field of $H = 3000$ oe at room temperature.

8.20. It has been found experimentally that in the transition from a gaseous to a condensed state the paramagnetic properties of atoms of the rare earth elements, contrary to the atoms of other elements, change very little. How is this explained?

8.21. In recent years the method of magnetic resonance has been widely used to investigate the magnetic properties of substances. It consists of the following: a paramagnetic substance is acted upon simultaneously by two magnetic fields—a "strong" constant field H and a variable field H_ν perpendicular to it. For certain definite values of the strength of the field H sharp maxima are observed in the absorption of the electromagnetic field energy.

(a) What is the explanation of this phenomenon?

(b) Show that a resonance takes place providing that $h\nu = g\mu_0 H$ where ν is the frequency of the field H_ν, g the Landé factor and μ_0 the Bohr magneton.

8.22. When two mutually orthogonal magnetic fields are applied to a paramagnetic substance (a strong constant field H and a weak variable field of frequency ν) a resonant absorption of the energy of the variable field by the substance is observed ("paramagnetic resonance"). In the simplest cases the maximum of the absorption occurs when

$$h\nu = g\mu_0 H,$$

where h is Planck's constant, g the Landé factor and μ_0 the Bohr magneton. Determine for what frequency one may expect the resonance to occur in a gas consisting of thallium atoms (in a $^2P_{1/2}$ state) in a field $H = 2000$ oe.

9. X-RAYS

1. The law of attenuation of the intensity of X-rays passing through a homogeneous substance is:

$$J = J_0 e^{-\mu d},$$

where J and J_0 are the intensities of the transmitted and the incident beams; μ is the coefficient of linear attenuation, which depends on the radiation wavelength and on the nature of the substance, d is the thickness of the layer.

2. The coefficients of absorption and scattering of X-rays are:

Name	Coefficient		
	Total absorption	True absorption	Scattering
Linear, cm^{-1}	$\mu = \tau + \sigma$	τ	σ
Mass, cm^2/g	$\dfrac{\mu}{\varrho}$	$\dfrac{\tau}{\varrho}$	$\dfrac{\sigma}{\varrho} \approx 0\cdot2$
Atomic, cm^2	$\mu_a = \dfrac{\mu}{\varrho}\dfrac{A}{N}$	$\tau_a = \dfrac{\tau}{\varrho}\dfrac{A}{N}$	$\sigma_a = \dfrac{\sigma}{\varrho}\dfrac{A}{N}$

Here ϱ is the density of the substance, A the atomic weight, and N Avogadro's number.

3. Approximate empirical expression for the mass coefficient of true absorption are:

$$\frac{\tau}{\varrho} = a\frac{\lambda^3 Z^4}{A} \ [\mathrm{cm^2/g}], \quad a = \begin{cases} 13\cdot6 \times 10^{-3} \ (\lambda < \lambda_K), \\ 1\cdot8 \times 10^{-3} \ (\lambda > \lambda_K), \end{cases}$$

where λ is the radiation wavelength in Å, λ_K the wavelength corresponding to the edge of the absorption K band of the substance, Z the atomic number of the element and A its atomic weight.

4. J. J. Thomson's formula for the atomic scattering, coefficient of X-rays is:

$$\sigma_a = \frac{8\pi}{3} \frac{Z e^4}{m^2 c^4},$$

where e and m are the charge and the mass of the electron, Z the atomic number, c the velocity of light.

5. The Bragg formula for the specular reflection of X-rays from the planes of a crystal is:

$$2d \sin \vartheta = k\lambda,$$

where d is the distance between the crystal planes for a given reflection, ϑ is the glancing angle, k the order of the spectrum, and λ the wavelength.

6. Moseley's law is

$$\bar{\nu} = R(Z - \sigma)^2 \left(\frac{1}{n_1^2} - \frac{1}{n_2^2} \right) [\text{cm}^{-1}],$$

where $\bar{\nu}$ is the wave number, R Rydberg's constant, σ a certain correction factor, Z the atomic number, and n_1 and n_2 the principal quantum numbers of the energy levels between which the transition occurs.

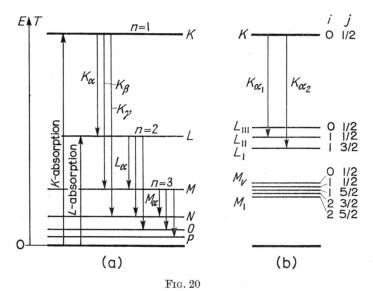

7. Figure 20 represents the X-rays terms and the corresponding transitions in the usually accepted notation: (a) the simplified term diagram (without fine structure); (b) the complete term diagram for the *K*, *L* and *M* shells.

Absorption and Scattering of X-rays

9.1. In a certain experimental arrangement 0·5 cm thick lead plates are used as an X-ray shield. The absorption coefficient of lead is 52·2 cm^{-1}. If the absorption coefficient of aluminum is 0·765 cm^{-1}, how thick should an aluminum absorber be, in order to give the same shielding as the lead?

9.2. When visible light passes through a layer of water 100 m thick, its intensity decreases by a factor of *e*. X-rays attenuate by the same factor in passing through a layer of water 5 cm thick. Determine the corresponding absorption coefficients and their ratio.

9.3. (a) How thick should an aluminum foil be for the K_α-rays of iron to be attenuated 10 times more than the K_α-rays of molybdenum? The mass absorption coefficients for these rays are 94 and 5·3 cm^2/g respectively.

(b) By how much will the intensity of the K_α-rays of molybdenum decrease in this case?

9.4. What is the main difference between the true absorption and the scattering of X-rays by a substance?

9.5. Using the Thomson formula for the atomic coefficient for scattering of X-rays find the number of electrons in the atoms of nitrogen, oxygen and fluorine, if their mass numbers and the value of the mass coefficient for scattering of X-rays (0·2 cm^2/g) are given. The universal constants are also assumed to be known.

9.6. Using the Thomson formula for the scattering of X-rays estimate the order of magnitude of the effective cross-section of one electron. Compare the radius of the cross-section obtained with the "classical" electron radius.

9.7. The true mass absorption coefficient of iron for X-rays of wavelength 0·209 Å is equal to 1·26 cm^2/g. Calculate the corresponding true atomic absorption coefficient.

9.8. Determine the ratio of the true mass coefficients of absorption for X-rays in the bones and the tissue of a human body. It is known that bones consists of calcium phosphate, $Ca_3(PO_4)_2$, and that the absorption in tissue is due mainly to the water it contains.

9.9. The dependence of the total mass coefficient of absorption for aluminum on the wavelength of the X-radiation is shown in Fig. 21.

(a) Estimate from this diagram the thickness of an aluminum foil which attenuates radiation of wavelength $\lambda_1 = 0.9$ Å ten times less than radiation of wavelength $\lambda_2 = 1.74$ Å (an X-ray filter).

(b) By what factor will the intensity of the radiation of wavelength λ_1 diminish in this case?

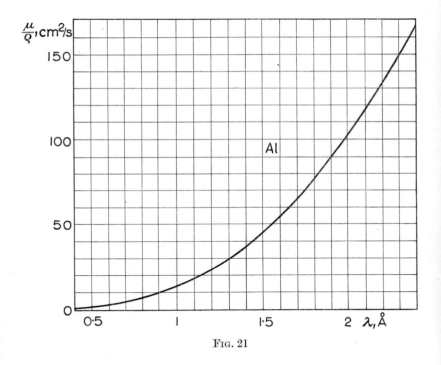

Fig. 21

9.10. Determine the change in the total mass coefficient of absorption for the edge of the K absorption band of molybdenum, i.e., find the ratio of magnitudes of μ and ϱ, measured immediately to the left and to the right of the K band edge (λ_K).

9.11. What metal must one use for a selectively absorptive X-ray filter which transmits K_α rays and at the same time considerably attenuates the K_β rays originating from the anti-cathode of an X-ray tube. Assume that the anti-cathode is made:

(a) of cobalt $(\lambda_{K\alpha} = 1.79 \text{ Å}, \lambda_{K\beta} = 1.62 \text{ Å})$;

(b) of zinc $\quad(\lambda_{K\alpha} = 1.43 \text{ Å}, \lambda_{K\beta} = 1.29 \text{ Å})$.

9.12. For very hard X-rays, whose frequency ν_i is considerably greater than the vibration eigenfrequencies ν of electrons in atoms, the dielectric constant of a substance is

$$\varepsilon = 1 - \frac{N_0 e^2}{\pi m \nu^2},$$

where e and m are the charge and the mass of the electron, and N_0 is the number of electrons per cm^3 of the substance. Find from this expression the phase and the group velocity of very hard X-rays in the material. Comment on the results obtained.

X-RAY SPECTRA

9.13. The best modern diffraction gratings have up to 1200 lines per mm. Show that for a beam of X-rays of wavelength 1 Å falling normally on such a grating the distance of the first order spectrum from the central maximum on a screen 1 m away is such that it is practically impossible to obtain a spectrum. How can one overcome this difficulty?

9.14. To determine absolutely the wavelength of X-rays one uses reflection from an ordinary diffraction grating. Calculate the wavelength, given that a grating with 100 lines per 1 mm makes a glancing angle of 20′ with the incoming beam of rays; the angle between the specularly reflected beam and the beam corresponding to the first order maximum is also 20′.

9.15. (a) Determine the crystal lattice constant of NaCl, given that the first order specular reflection of 2·1 Å X-rays from the natural face of this crystal occurs at a glancing angle of 22° 10′.

(b) From the value obtained for the NaCl lattice calculate Avogadro's number. The density of NaCl is 2·1 g/cm^3.

9.16. Show that for a given direction of incident rays, the interference maxima from a simple cubic lattice will arise only for certain definite wavelengths.

9.17. Explain why one uses continuous spectrum radiation to obtain the diffraction pattern from a monocrystal and why, when monochromatic radiation is used, the crystal is rotated.

9.18. Explain why every chemical element gives a characteristic spectrum, regardless whether it is in a chemically free state or in a compound. What happens to the optical spectral in these two cases?

9.19. (a) What is the difference between X-ray terms and optical terms?

(b) Set up on a single diagram the scheme of the X-ray and the optical terms.

9.20. Starting with which elements can one expect the emission of the characteristic K and L X-ray series?

9.21. What is the significance of Moseley's law? Give the physical meaning of the correction term σ introduced in the expression for this law.

9.22. Calculate the wave number, the wavelength and the energy of the quantum corresponding to the K_α line of silver.

9.23. The wavelengths of the K_α lines of the following elements are known: magnesium (9·87 Å), aluminum (8·32 Å) and silicon (7·11 Å). Calculate the σ corrections for these lines.

9.24. Show that for the K_α lines of heavier elements, such as for example tin (0·492 Å), caesium (0·402 Å) and tungsten (0·210 Å) the correction factors σ deviate considerably from 1.

9.25. Calculate the values of the correction factor for the following wavelengths in the spectrum of copper:

1·54 Å (K_α), 1·39 Å (K_β), 1·378 Å (K_γ) and 1·377 Å (the absorption edge). Use a diagram to make clear the origin of these lines. Explain the difference in the calculated correction factors.

9.26. (a) Estimate the critical voltages on an X-ray tube for which the K_α lines of platinum, gold and uranium begin to appear.

(b) What must one know to calculate the exact values of these voltages?

9.27. What happens to the spectrum of X-rays emitted by the anticathode as the voltage on the tube is gradually increased?

9.28. The short wave limit of the continuous X-ray spectrum of aluminum corresponds to a wavelength of 5 Å. Can one then observe the K lines in the characteristic spectrum?

9.29. Determine the critical voltage in an X-ray tube necessary to excite the K series of silver, given that the wavelength of its absorption band limit is 0·4845 Å. Explain why the wavelength of the K_α line is longer than the wavelength of the absorption edge.

9.30. (a) Find the wave number ratio of the K_α line of copper and the principal line of the Lyman series for hydrogen.

(b) For what hydrogen-like ion will the wavelength of the principal line of the Lyman series be approximately equal to the wavelength of the L_α line of vanadium, its correction factor being $\sigma = 6\cdot5$?

9.31. (a) Calculate the velocity of the electrons knocked out of the K shell of molybdenum atoms by the K_α rays of silver?

(b) What is the maximum velocity of these electrons, when molybdenum is irradiated with the characteristic radiation of silver?

9.32. A small sphere of carbon that serves as the inner electrode of a spherical condenser is irradiated with the K_α rays of aluminum and emission of photoelectrons is observed. The energy spectrum of the electrons is analysed by varying a retarding potential U. (This is the method of P. I. Lukirski). As the retarding potential is increased up to $U = 1210$ V, a first sharp decrease in the photoelectric current is observed. Explain the origin of the photoelectrons that correspond to the given value of U and find the energy value of the corresponding X-ray term of the carbon atom.

9.33. Estimate the wavelength corresponding to the end of the L absorption band for aluminium if the wavelength of the K_α line (8·32 Å) is known as well as λ_K the absorption edge of the K series (see the tables in the Appendix).

9.34. (a) Why is the edge of the K series band in the absorption spectrum simple, that of the L series triple, that of the M series quintuple, etc.?

(b) Show that the X-ray emission spectra consist of doublets, just like the spectra of the alkali metals.

9.35. What is the spectral symbol of the X-ray term that corresponds to the state of an atom directly after an electron with quantum numbers: $j = 3/2$ and $l = 1$ is knocked out of one of the closed shells (i.e. before X-ray emission has taken place).

9.36. From the selection rules for the quantum numbers l and j determine the number of spectral lines resulting from the transitions between the following atomic X-ray terms $K \to L$, $K \to M$ and $L \to M$.

9.37. Calculate in electron volts and set up the diagram of the K, L and M terms for a vanadium atom, using the following data: the wavelength of the K_β line is 2·28 Å, that of the L_α line 25·9 Å; the value of the absorption edge of the K series given in the Appendix.

9.38. Determine the energy necessary to knock out a K electron from a rubidium atom, given that its absorption edge is $\lambda = 6\cdot 8$ Å.

9.39. The values of the following terms of a uranium atom (measured in Rydberg units, T/R), are $K(8477\cdot0)$, $L_I(1264\cdot3)$, $L_{II}(1543\cdot1)$ and $L_{III}(1603\cdot5)$.

(a) Find the wavelengths corresponding to the possible transitions between these terms.

(b) Determine the excitation potentials of the K and L series of uranium.

REFERENCE

1. cf., for instance, A. H. COMPTON and S. K. ALLISON, *X-Rays in Theory and Experiment*, Van Nostrand, 2nd Edn. 1935.

10. MANY ELECTRON ATOMS.
THE PERIODIC SYSTEM OF ELEMENTS

1. The following notation is used to describe the distribution of electrons in an atom:

Shells	Subshells
$K(n = 1)$	$1s$
$L(n = 2)$	$2s, 2p$
$M(n = 3)$	$3s, 3p, 3d$
$N(n = 4)$	$4s, 4p, 4d, 4f$
etc.	

2. The Pauli principle states that:
in an atom there cannot be two or more electrons with identical quantum numbers n, l, m_l, m_s (or n, l, j, m_j).

3. The Hund rules for defining the ground term of an atom state that:

(a) The term of least energy is that which, for a given electron configuration, has the greatest possible value of total spin S_{max} and the greatest value possible with this S_{max} of the total orbital quantum number L.

(b) For the ground term $J = |L - S|$, if the subshell is less than half filled, and $J = L + S$ if the subshell is more than half filled.

10.1. List the possible terms for the following atomic states:
$$^2S, \ ^2P, \ ^4P \quad \text{and} \quad ^5D.$$

10.2. Determine the degeneracies of the following terms:
$$^2D_{3/2}, \ ^3F_3, \ ^1F.$$

10.3. Assuming that the spin and the orbital angular momentum do not interact (how can this be achieved experimentally?), find the number of possible states of an atom whose quantum numbers S and L are known.

10.4. Show that the sum $\Sigma (2J + 1)$ over all possible values of the quantum number J for given S and L is equal to the product $(2S + 1)(2L + 1)$. What is the physical meaning of this product?

10.5. Find the number of electrons in atoms which have the following levels filled in the ground state:

(a) the K- and L-shells, the $3s$ subshell and one half of the $3p$-subshell;

(b) the K-, L- and M-shells and the $4s$-, $4p$- and $4d$-subshells. What atoms are these?

10.6. What is the maximum number of the electrons in an atom that can share the following common, quantum numbers:

(a) n, l, m_l;

(b) l;

(c) n?

10.7. Tabulate all possible values of the quantum numbers n, l, m_l, m_s for the electrons filling:

(a) the L-shell

(b) the M-shell.

10.8. Why does the actual periodic table of elements not correspond to the "ideal" one? This latter is constructed under the assumption that electrons fill the states with least possible quantum numbers in succession.

10.9. Where in the periodic table does the first deviation from the "ideal" scheme in the order of filling the electronic shells occur? What causes such deviations?

10.10. Using the Pauli principle show that the angular momenta P_L, P_S, and P_J of closed atomic subshells and shells are all zero.

10.11. Find the number of possible terms in an excited carbon whose electronic configuration is $1s^2 2s^2 2p^1 3d^1$.

10.12. Determine the possible values of the quantum numbers L and S and the type of terms of an atom that has all subshells completely filled except two: $4f^1 5d^1$. The coupling is Russell–Saunders.

10.13. (a) Show that one can determine the ground state terms of hydrogen, helium, lithium and beryllium atoms using Pauli's principle alone.

(b) Verify that one can not determine the ground states of nitrogen and oxygen atoms by means of the Pauli principle alone. Find them by the Hund rule.

10.14. Determine the ground states of atoms whose symbols and electron configuration are:

(a) Y: krypton shell $+ 4d^{15}s^2$;

(b) Zr: krypton shell $+ 4d^{25}s^2$.

10.15. The maganese atom in its ground state has one unfilled subshell, which is exactly half filled by five electrons. Determine the electron configuration of this subshell and the ground term of the atom.

10.16. Find the possible types of terms for a configuration of three equivalent p electrons, and use the Hund rule to determine the fundamental term.

Note: Electrons having the same quantum numbers n and l are said to be equivalent.

10.17. Determine the possible types of terms for the electron configurations of one and of five electrons: p^1 and p^5.

10.18. Determine the number of the possible states (terms) for a configuration of k equivalent l-electrons: nl^k, where n is the principal and l the orbital quantum number. Consider in particular the case: nd^3.

10.19. Calculate the effective magnetic moment corresponding to the ground term of a configuration of three equivalent d-electrons: nd^3.

10.20. Using general arguments, give the configurations of equivalent electrons whose possible states (terms) are the same as in the following electron configurations: np^1, nd^3 and nf^5.

10.21. Determine the possible values of the quantum numbers L and S for an atom with the electron configuration $ns'n'p^2$ where $n \neq n'$. Find the possible types of terms.

10.22. Which of the listed properties of elements change periodically with the atomic number:

(a) valency;

(b) atomic volume;

(c) melting point;

(d) characteristic X-ray spectrum;

(e) ionization potential?

What causes the differences in these properties?

11. MOLECULES

1. The angular momentum of a rotating molecule is
$$P_r = \hbar \sqrt{R(R+1)},$$
where $\hbar$ is Planck's constant ($\hbar = 1{\cdot}05 \times 10^{-27}$ erg . sec); R is the rotational quantum number, $R = 0, 1, 2, \ldots$.

2. The rotational energy of a rigid diatomic molecule is
$$E_R = hBR(R+1),$$
where h is Planck's constant ($h = 6{\cdot}62 \times 10^{-27}$ erg . sec), $B = h/8\pi^2 I$ the rotational constant, I the moment of inertia of the molecule relative to the figure axis and R the rotational quantum number, $R = 0, 1, 2, \ldots$.

3. The vibrational energy of a diatomic molecule for the case of harmonic oscillations (a quantum oscillator) is
$$E_v = h\nu \left(v + \frac{1}{2} \right),$$
where
$$\nu = \frac{1}{2\pi} \sqrt{\frac{k}{\mu}}$$
is the oscillation frequency of the nuclei (k is the elastic force modulus,
$$\mu = \frac{m_1 m_2}{m_1 + m_2}$$
the reduced mass of the molecule); v is the vibrational quantum number, $v = 0, 1, 2, \ldots$.

4. The vibrational energy of a diatomic molecule for anharmonic oscillations (when the force of interaction between the nuclei cannot be considered elastic) may be approximated by the following formula:[1]
$$E_v = h\nu(v + \tfrac{1}{2}) - xh\nu(v + \tfrac{1}{2})^2,$$
where x is the anharmonicity parameter.

78

5. The average energy of a quantum oscillator is

$$\bar{E} = \frac{h\nu}{2} + \frac{h\nu}{e^{h\nu/kT} - 1},$$

where ν is the oscillation frequency, k the Boltzmann constant and T the absolute temperature.

6. The usual notation for the electronic states of a diatomic molecule is

$$\lambda = 0, 1, 2, 3, \ldots$$
symbol: $\sigma, \pi, \delta, \varphi, \ldots$
$$\Lambda = 0, 1, 2, 3, \ldots$$
symbol: $\Sigma, \Pi, \Delta, \Phi, \ldots$

Here λ is the quantum number corresponding to the projection of the orbital angular momentum of an individual electron on the axis of the molecule; Λ is the quantum number of the electronic shell of the molecule $\Lambda = \Sigma \lambda_i$.

DEGREES OF FREEDOM. ROTATION AND VIBRATIONS OF MOLECULES

11.1. Determine the vibrational degrees of freedom of the following n-atomic molecules (Fig. 22);
(a) CO_2, C_1H_2 (linear molecules);
(b) H_2O, CH_4, UF_6.

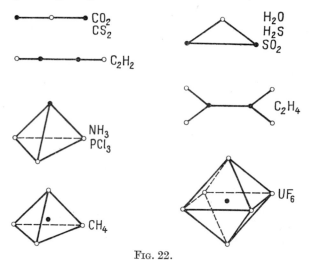

FIG. 22.

11.2. Find the mean energy of the molecules PCl_3 and C_2H_2 (Fig. 22), when all their degress of freedom (translational, rotational and vibrational) are excited.

11.3. A gas in thermal equilibrium consists of n-atomic molecules with all their degrees of freedom (translational, rotational and vibrational) excited. Determine the pressure such a gas exerts on the walls of a vessel, assuming that the energy of excitation of 1 cm³ of gas is E.

11.4. Determine the angular frequency of rotation of S_2 and HI molecules, assuming that their first rotational states are excited. Take the value of the distance between the nuclei of these molecules from the tables in the Appendix.

11.5. Calculate the temperatures for which the mean kinetic energy of translation of the H_2, O_2 and Cl_2 molecules is equal to their rotational energy in the first excited state. Take the necessary data from the tables in the Appendix.

11.6. What is the minimum "rotational quantum" of energy of the following linear molecules (Fig. 22):

(a) F_2, the distance between its nuclei is given in the tables in the Appendix.

(b) CO_2, the distance between adjoining nuclei is 1·13 Å.

(c) C_2H_2, the distance between the adjoining nuclei is 1·20 Å (C—C) and 1·06 Å (C—H).

11.7. Determine the degree of degeneracy of the energy level with rotational quantum number r of a diatomic molecule.

11.8. Give reasons, why in the explanation of specific heats of diatomic molecules in the kinetic theory of gases only two rotational degrees of freedom are taken into account. The diameter of nuclei is approximately equal to 3×10^{-13} A cm, where A is the number of nucleons (neutrons and protons) in the nucleus.

11.9. Write the approximate quantum expression for the total energy of a diatomic molecule, assuming it is not acted on by external forces, which includes the rotational and vibrational contributions.

11.10. Find the ratio of excitation energies of the first rotational and vibrational levels of a molecule. Calculate this ratio for the molecules H_2, HI and I_2. The necessary data are given in the Appendix.

11.11. From the frequency of the vibrational mode of a chlorine molecule and the distance between its nuclei calculate up to which rotational level a molecule should be excited in order that its rotational energy become equal to the excitation energy of the first vibrational excited state.

11.12. Calculate the energies necessary to dissociate each of the molecules H_2 and HCl, both of them being in the vibrational states with quantum number $v = 2$. The dissociation energies of these molecules are assumed given (see the tables).

11.13. Determine the value of the maximum vibrational energy of a Cl_2 molecule, whose anharmonicity parameter is $x = 7.08 \times 10^{-3}$. See the tables in the Appendix for the vibrational frequency of this molecule.

11.14. Find the anharmonicity parameter x of a P_2 molecule, whose vibrational frequency and dissociation energy are given (take them from the tables). Note that when this molecule is dissociated one of the atoms proves to be in a 1·66 eV excited state.

11.15. Using the Boltzmann distribution, calculate what fraction of oxygen molecules at a temperature of 2000°K will be found in states corresponding to the first and the second vibrational levels ($v = 1$ and 2). The coefficient of the elastic force for the oxygen molecule is 1.18×10^6 d/cm.

11.16. Use the Boltzmann distribution law to determine the ratio of the numbers of hydrogen molecules in the first excited rotational and vibrational energy states. The temperature of the gas is 3000°K. Take the rest of the necessary data from the tables.

11.17. Use the Boltzmann distribution law and the expression for the energy of a quantum oscillator to derive the formula for the average energy of an oscillator at a given temperature.

11.18. Calculate the average vibrational energies of a hydrogen molecule at temperatures of 300° and 3000°K. Compare the results with those obtained for the same temperatures from classical physics. Take the value of the vibrational frequency of a hydrogen molecule from the tables.

11.19. (a) Starting from the expression for the average energy of a quantum oscillator obtain the temperature dependence of the molar "vibrational" specific heat and draw a graph of this function.

(b) Estimate from the graph the temperature at which the "vibrational" specific heat of chlorine gas differs from the classical value by 10 per cent. The eigenfrequency of a chlorine molecule is 1.7×10^{13} sec^{-1}.

11.20. Figure 23 represents the dependence of the specific heat of a diatomic gas on temperature. Explain the qualitative nature of this dependence and give the numerical values of the molar specific heats corresponding to the points C_1, C_2 and C_3.

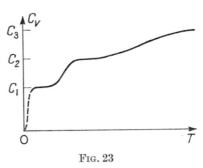

FIG. 23

MOLECULAR SPECTRA. RAMAN SCATTERING
OF LIGHT

11.21. How do molecular spectra differ from atomic spectra? Explain the regularities found in molecular spectra, the association of the individual lines into bands, and of bands into groups and the presence in a spectrum of several groups of bands.

11.22. Starting from the expression for the rotational energy of a rigid diatomic molecule, show that:

(a) the distances between neighbouring energy levels increase with the quantum number;

(b) the intervals (in wave numbers) between the spectral lines corresponding to allowed transitions are equal.

11.23. (a) Show that the wavelengths of the purely rotational spectrum of a rigid diatomic molecule is desribed by the following expression

$$\lambda = \frac{2\pi c I}{\hbar R},$$

where c is the velocity of light, I the moment of inertia of the molecule, and R the rotational quantum number of the upper levels, $R = 1, 2, 3$.

(b) Find the change in the angular momentum of a nitrogen molecule after it emits a spectral line of wavelength $\lambda = 1250\,\mu$ belonging to a purely rotational band of the spectrum.

11.24. The wave numbers of a series of lines of the purely rotational spectrum of an HCl molecule are:

$$124.30,\ 145.03,\ 165.63,\ 185.86\ \text{and}\ 206.38\ \text{cm}^{-1}.$$

Hence calculate:
  (a) the moment of inertia of the molecule;
  (b) the distance between its nuclei;
  (c) its angular velocity in the first rotational level.

11.25. Show that for a transition between neighbouring vibrational levels the frequency of the emitted light coincides with the vibrational frequency of the nuclei (when their interaction is of the character produced by an elastic force).

11.26. Find the relative isotopic shift of a line in a purely rotational band of the spectrum of a mixture of HCl^{35} and HCl^{37} molecules.

11.27. What is the ratio of the relative isotopic shifts in purely vibrational bands of the spectra of the following two mixtures of molecules: C_2^{12}, $C^{12}C^{13}$ and H^1Cl^{35}, H^2Cl^{35}?

11.28. Determine the difference in the dissociation energies of hydrogen molecules consisting of light and heavy hydrogen atoms (H_2^1 and H_2^2) given that the vibrational frequency of the molecule H_2^1 is $\bar{\nu} = 4395.2\ \text{cm}^{-1}$.

11.29. From Pauli's principle determine the maximum number of the σ-, π-, and δ-electrons in a diatomic molecule.

11.30. (a) What is the parity of the multiplicities of the electron states in the following molecules: CO, O_2, NO and OH.

(b) Determine the possible types of terms of diatomic molecules whose electronic states are: $^1\Sigma$, $^3\Sigma$ and $^2\Pi$.

11.31. Taking into account the selection rules for the quantum numbers Λ and S ($\Delta\Lambda = 0, \pm 1, \Delta S = 0$), determine the number of possible transitions of a diatomic molecule (between purely electronic levels) in which one electron is in a σ- and the other in a π-state.

11.32. The Raman scattering of light is explained classically by the fact that the forced vibrations (the incident light) are modulated by the vibrations of the molecules of the substance and, that as a result of this, the scattered light can be represented as a superposition of two vibrations of somewhat different frequencies v_1 and v_2. Find v_1 and v_2 for the case when monochromatic light of wavelength 4000 Å is modulated by a frequency of 10^{12} c/s.

11.33. A light quantum of 4350 Å wavelength is scattered on a molecule of NO and as a result its wavelength increases by 400 Å. Hence find the change in the vibrational quantum number of the molecule, if n, the elastic force modulus, is 1.54×10^6 d/cm.

11.34. A scattering substance consists of diatomic molecules, one of whose atoms belongs to the oxygen isotope O^{16}. Determine to what element the other atom belongs, given that for Raman scattering of light the Stokes lines are displaced by $\Delta \bar{v} = 2169$ cm^{-1} from the fundamental line and the elastic force modulus of the molecules is $k = 1.91 \times 10^6$ d/cm.

11.35. The wavelengths of the Stokes lines of a certain line in Raman scattering of light on HF molecules are 2670 and 3430 Å. Hence calculate the vibrational frequency of the molecules and also the elastic force coefficient.

11.36. The vibrational Raman spectrum is observed in a gas consisting of chlorine molecules at room temperature ($T = 293°$K). By how many degrees should the temperature of the gas be raised so that the ratio of the intensities of the anti-stokes lines to the Stokes lines should change by a factor of 2.

11.37. Explain why the fluorescent spectrum is more complex than the exciting spectrum. Why does it contain wavelengths which are equal or larger than the wavelengths of the exciting light (the Stokes rule)? How does one explain the observed deviations from the Stokes rule?

11.38. Describe the principle of action and the purpose of a maser. How are molecules of a given excitation energy obtained from it? What is the basic distinctive property of this type of generator?

REFERENCE

1. G. HERZBERG, *Molecular Spectra and Molecular Structure*, Van Nostrand 2nd Edn. (1950). Vol. I, p. 92.

TRANSMUTATIONS OF ATOMIC NUCLEI

1. The law of radioactive decay is

$$N = N_0 e^{-\lambda t},$$

where λ is the decay constant and N_0 the initial number of radioactive atoms.

2. The half-life T and the mean life τ of radioactive atoms are given by:

$$T = \frac{\ln 2}{\lambda}, \quad \tau = \frac{1}{\lambda}.$$

3. The law of accumulation of radioactive atoms forming at a constant rate q is given by:

$$N = \frac{q}{\lambda} (1 - e^{-\lambda t}).$$

4. The activity of a radioactive sample is:

$$n = -\frac{dN}{dt} = \lambda N,$$

where N is the number of radioactive atoms.

5. The condition for radioactive equilibrium is

$$\lambda_p N_p = \lambda_d N_d,$$

where the indices p and d refer respectively to the parent and daughter substances. Such a state occurs after an interval of time considerably greater than the half-life of the daughter substance and when in addition $\lambda_p \ll \lambda_d$.

6. The mass decrement Δ and the packing fraction p of a nucleus are defined by:

$$\Delta = M - A,$$

$$p = \frac{M - A}{A},$$

where M is the isotope mass and A the mass number (the isotope mass rounded off to the nearest integer).

7. The binding energy E of a nucleus and its mass defect ΔM are defined by the expression:

$$E = \Delta M c^2 = [Z m_p + (A - Z) m_n - M] c^2,$$

where Z is the atomic number of the nuclide, m_p and m_n the proton and the neutron masses, and M the mass of the nucleus.

8. The energy released in a nuclear reaction $m + M \to m' + M'$ is:

$$Q = [(m + M) - (m' + M')] c^2.$$

The reaction is said to be exothermic when $Q > 0$, and endothermic when $Q < 0$.

9. The threshold energy of a nuclear reaction, i.e. the minimum kinetic energy of the bombarding particle that can produce an endothermic reaction, is expressed by:

$$E_{\mathrm{thr}} = \frac{m + M}{M} |Q|,$$

where M is the mass of a nucleus at rest, bombarded by a particle of mass m, and Q is the energy of the reaction.

When a bombarding particle has a kinetic energy equal to the threshold value, the relative velocity of the particles produced in the reaction is zero.

10. Geiger's expression for the alpha particle range in air at n.t.p. is:

$$R = a v^3 \quad [\mathrm{cm}],$$

where v is the initial velocity of the alpha particle and α, a constant, is $9 \cdot 6 \times 10^{-28} \sec^3/\mathrm{cm}^2$.

RADIOACTIVITY

12.1. From the radioactive decay law derive the expression for the mean life of radioactive nuclei.

12.2. The radioactive decay constants for uranium, radium and radon are respectively:

$$4 \cdot 9 \times 10^{-18}, \ 1 \cdot 37 \times 10^{-11} \ \text{and} \ 2 \cdot 09 \times 10^{-6} \sec^{-1}.$$

Calculate the mean lives and half-lives of these nuclei.

12.3. Determine the quantity of lead formed from 1 kg of pure U^{238} during a time equal to the age of the earth ($2 \cdot 5 \times 10^9$ years). The effective half-life for this uranium isotope to decay to Pb is $4 \cdot 5 \times 10^9$ years.

12.4. (a) Natural uranium ore contains one radium atom for every $2 \cdot 78 \times 10^6$ uranium atoms. Determine the decay half-life of uranium, given that the half-life of radium is 1620 years.

(b) From the result of (a) determine the age of a mineral containing 1 atom of lead for every two atoms of uranium.

12.5. The curie, a unit of radioactivity, is defined as the number of decays occurring in 1 g of radium in 1 sec. Find this number, given that the half-life of radium is 1620 years.

12.6. The half-life of U^{235} is $8 \cdot 5 \times 10^8$ years. What is the specific activity of this isotope, i.e. what is the number of decays occurring in 1 sec per 1 g of the substance? Express the activity obtained in μC.

12.7. At present the method of radioactive tracers is widely used in various types of research. What does it consist of? Name some fields of research where this method could be used.

12.8. One cm^3 of a solution containing the artificial radioactive isotope Na^{24} with a decay activity of $N_0 = 200$ particles/sec, was injected into the blood of a man. The activity of 1 cm^3 of the blood, taken after a time $t = 5$ hr proved to be $N = 16$ particles/min. Assuming the half-life of Na^{24} to be known (see Appendix 9) determine the volume of blood in the man's body.

12.9. Calculate the total energy liberated when an alpha particle is ejected from a Po^{213} nucleus, given that such an alpha particle has an energy of $8 \cdot 34$ MeV.

12.10. A nucleus of Pu^{239} decays by ejecting a $5 \cdot 3$ MeV alpha particle. Given that the half-life of Pu^{239} is 24,000 years, determine the quantity of heat produced by 1 cm^3 of it in the course of 1 year. Neglect the products of further decay. The density of plutonium is 19 g/cm^3.

12.11. What isotope is formed from alpha-active Th^{232} as the result of four alpha and two beta decays?

12.12. Calculate the total alpha activity in curies of a sample containing radium in equilibrium with its decay products. The activity of the radium itself is assumed equal to 1 C.

ANP 4

12.13. As an element A with a decay constant λ_A decays, an element B with a decay constant λ_B is formed. Derive the expression for the change in time of the number of radioactive nuclei B, assuming that at $t = 0$ the sample consisted entirely of $N_A(0)$ atoms of A.

12.14. Show that when the chain $A \to B \to C$ of nuclear transformation occurs, and provided that $\lambda_A < \lambda_B$, then after a time considerably longer than the mean life of the stabler of the two nuclei, the ratio of the substances A and B will remain constant in time.

12.15. The radioisotope RaA decays with a half-life of T_A $= 3$ min. The resulting RaB decays in turn with a half-life of 27 min. Assuming that at $t = 0$ the sample contained only RaA:

(a) find after how long a time the quantity of RaB will be at a maximum?

(b) draw a graph illustrating the change of the quantity of RaB in time;

(c) show how the curve changes for various ratios of the half-lives of parent and daughter isotopes.

12.16. After what interval of time will the specific activity of a thallium isotope, which has a half-life of 3·5 years, be 10 μC/g, if its rate of formation is $q = 10^{10}$ atom/cm^3 sec? The density of thallium is 11·85 g/cm^3.

NUCLEAR REACTIONS

12.17. Express in MeV the rest mass of an electron and of the atomic mass unit.[2] How do the physical and chemical scales of atomic masses differ?

12.18. Show that in calculating the mass defect or the binding energy of nuclei we can use the masses of the atoms themselves and compare them with the sum of the masses of a corresponding number of hydrogen atoms and neutrons.

12.19. (a) Obtain an expression for the mass defect of a nucleus as a function of its mass decrement.

(b) Calculate the mass decrements and the mass defects of the nuclei of the following atoms: He^4, C^{12} and O^{16}.

12.20. Calculate the mass defect and the binding energy of the following atoms: deuterium, tritium and Be^9.

12.21. The isotopic weights of a tritium and a helium atom are $3 \cdot 01700$ MU and $3 \cdot 01698$ MU respectively. Find the mass defects of the two isotopes (in mass units and in MeV) and explain their difference.

12.22. What is the minimum energy necessary to split the O^{16} nucleus into four equal parts?

12.23. From the tables of atomic masses find the minimum energy necessary to separate (a) a proton (b) a neutron from the nucleus of He^4. Explain the difference in these results.

12.24. The end-point energy of electrons in the beta-decay of He^6 is $3 \cdot 57$ MeV. Find the mass of the He^6 atom.

12.25. (a) How should one determine the energy liberated in the β^+-decay of nuclei when using the *atomic* masses.

(b) Calculate the maximum energy of the positrons in the beta-decay of C^{11} nuclei.

12.26. A C^{11} nucleus at rest emits a positron of maximum energy. Estimate the recoil energy of the nucleus.

12.27. Find the total energy (in MeV) liberated in the reaction $Li^7 + p \rightarrow 2\alpha$, from the known values of the binding energy per nucleon of Li^7 ($5 \cdot 61$ MeV) and He^4 ($7 \cdot 06$ MeV).

12.28. The energy produced in the synthesis of two deuterons to form a He^4 nucleus is $23 \cdot 8$ MeV. What is the difference of the binding energies per nucleon in the alpha particle and the deuteron?

12.29. Find the energy liberated in the following reactions:

(a) $Be^9(d, \alpha)Li^7$;

(b) $H^2(d, p)H^3$;

(c) $Li^6(p, \alpha)He^3$.

12.30. When Li^6 nuclei are bombarded by deuterons the following two nuclear reactions take place:

$$Be^7 + n, \quad \text{and}$$
$$He^4 + He^3 + n.$$

Compare the values of the energies liberated in these reactions and explain their difference.

12.31. Find the velocity of the products of the nuclear reaction $B^{10}(n, \alpha)Li^7$, assuming that the neutrons are thermal and the B^{10} nuclei are initially at rest.

4*

12.32. (a) Why is an extremely high temperature necessary for thermonuclear reactions to take place?

(b) Estimate the order of magnitude of temperature necessary for the mean thermal energy of the H^2 nuclei to be sufficiently great to overcome the Coulomb potential barrier, which is maximum when the deuterons are a distance of 5 fermi apart. How can one explain the fact that fusion takes place at a temperature lower than that calculated?

12.33. Determine the minimum energy of the γ-quantum required for the photofission of Li and Be nuclei according to following reactions:

(a) $Li^7(\gamma, n)Li^6$;
(b) $Be^9(\gamma, n)2He^4$.

12.34. In an experiment on photofission of deuterons 2·62 MeV gamma quanta were used. The protons produced were registered by observing their tracks in a Wilson cloud chamber placed in a magnetic field of strength $H = 4400$ oe. Determine the binding energy of a deuteron, if the radius of curvature of protons in the cloud chamber is found to be 14·5 cm.

12.35. Show that when particles of mass m collide with a nucleus of mass M at rest, the threshold kinetic energy of the bombarding particles m necessary for the endothermic nuclear reaction. $m + M \rightarrow m' + M'$ to take place is given by

$$E_{thr} = \frac{m + M}{M} \, |Q| \,,$$

where m and M are the masses of the particles, and Q is the reaction energy.

12.36. (a) Determine the total kinetic energy of the products of the nuclear reaction $Li^7(p, n)Be^7$ when the bombarding protons have the threshold kinetic energy. The lithium nuclei are assumed to be at rest.

(b) Find the velocity of the Be^7 nuclei under these conditions.

12.37. In the collision of a 1·2 MeV deuteron with a deuteron at rest the $H^2(d, p)H^3$ reaction takes place. As the result of this reaction a proton moving at right angles to the direction of motion of the deuteron has a kinetic energy of 3·33 MeV. Determine the reaction energy.

12.38. The energy of the exothermic nuclear reaction $Be^9(\alpha, n)C^{12}$ is $Q = 5 \cdot 7$ MeV. Determine the kinetic energy of the neutrons that fly at right angles to the direction of the $5 \cdot 3$ MeV bombarding particles.

12.39. A lithium target is bombarded by a beam of $2 \cdot 7$ MeV protons and the reaction $Li^7 + p \to 2\alpha$ takes place. The two resulting alpha particles are observed to have the same energy.

(a) Determine the range in air at n.t.p. of the alpha particles.

(b) Find the angle between their directions of motion.

Nuclear Fission. The Utilization of Nuclear Energy

12.40. The Soviet physicists K. A. Petrzhak and G. N. Flerov observed experimentally that, in addition to undergoing alpha decay, U^{235} nuclei can also undergo spontaneous fission. Find the ratio of the intensities of these two processes, given that the alpha decay half-life of U^{235} is $8 \cdot 5 \times 10^8$ years and that the mean life of U^{235} nuclei for spontaneous fission is of the order of 3×10^{17} years.

12.41. The excitation energy necessary for the fission of the nucleus formed when a U^{235} nucleus captures a neutron must not be less than $5 \cdot 2$ MeV. Can this reaction take place if a U^{235} nucleus captures a thermal neutron?

12.42. What minimum kinetic energy must a neutron captured by a U^{235} nucleus have for the resulting compound nucleus to undergo fission? The activation energy of the compound nucleus is approximately 6 MeV.

12.43. When a fission process takes place as the result of the capture of a thermal neutron by a U^{235} nucleus, two fission fragments and two neutrons are produced. Estimate the energy freed in this process, given that the average binding energy per nucleon is $7 \cdot 8$ MeV in the fissioned nucleus and $8 \cdot 6$ MeV in the fission fragments.

12.44. A sample of natural uranium is exposed to a thermal neutron flux of 10^{10} neutron/cm^2 sec. Determine the thermal energy produced in 1 cm^3 of the sample as the result of the fission of U^{235} nuclei, assuming that their cross-section under the conditions of the experiment is 590 barns. The energy liberated per fission is assumed to be equal to 200 MeV. Take the other necessary data from the tables.

12.45. What is the role of the moderator used to obtain a controlled nuclear chain reaction in nuclear reactors? What must be the properties of such a moderator?

12.46. Find the maximum fraction of the kinetic energy (in per cent) lost by a neutron in elastic collisions with the following nuclei at rest:

(a) H^2, (b) Be^9, (c) C^{12} and (d) U^{238}.

12.47. (a) The initial kinetic energy of a neutron is E_0. Find the mean energy $\bar{E}$ of the neutron after one single elastic collision with a proton, assuming that the scattering is isotropic in the center of mass system.

(b) Calculate the average value of the angle of scattering for this reaction.

12.48. A fast 7 MeV neutron is slowed down in hydrogen. Assume that in every elastic scattering collision with the nuclei of the moderator the neutron deviates on the average by an angle of 45° from its direction of motion prior to the collision. Find the number of collisions necessary for the energy of the neutron to decrease to the average thermal energy corresponding to the temperature $T = 300°K$.

12.49. Uranium U-235 in a nuclear reactor is in the form of thin rods immersed in a moderator (a heterogeneous reactor). Estimate the fraction of energy produced by absorption of radiation in the moderator of such a reactor, as a result of the fission of uranium nuclei, assuming that on the average the energy produced in each fission process is distributed as follows:

160 MeV—kinetic energy of the fission fragments,
 5 MeV—kinetic energy of the neutrons and
10 MeV each carried off by gamma and beta radiation.

12.50. What is the multiplication factor of a reactor? How does the power of a reactor change with its multiplication factor k:

(a) $k < 1$; (b) $k = 1$; (c) $k < 1$?

12.51. Estimate the time in which the power of a reactor with a multiplication factor $k = 1·06$ increases by a factor of $\eta = 10^6$.

The mean life time of one generation of neutrons in a reactor is estimated to be $\tau \sim 0\cdot 1$ sec.

12.52. Calculate the mass of U^{235} undergoing fission in the explosion of an atomic bomb with a 30,000 ton TNT equivalent. The heat equivalent of TNT is assumed to be about 1 cal/g and the energy produced per fission is of the order of 200 MeV.

12.53. The motors of the atomic ice-breaker "Lenin" can produce 44,000 horsepower. Find the consumption of nuclear fuel per day in the reactor of the ice-breaker assuming that it is 20 per cent efficient. The average energy produced per fission of a U^{235} nucleus is about 200 MeV. Compare the result obtained with the daily amount of 7000 cal/kg coal needed to obtain the same power with an efficiency of 80 per cent.

12.54. Compare the thermal effects arising as the result of the consumption of 1 kg of nuclear fuel:

(a) in fission of pure U^{235} (each fission process produces about 200 MeV of energy);

(b) in the thermonuclear fusion process: $H^2 + H^2 \rightarrow He^4$.

What amounts of 7 kcal/g coal are necessary to produce the same thermal effects as in the above processes?

12.55. At present man uses about 1400 thousand millions of kWh of energy in one year. What is the mass equivalent of this energy? Estimate from the data of the preceding problem the amount of (a) coal, (b) uranium and (c) deuterium necessary to produce the same amount of energy. Take all the necessary data from the preceding problem.

REFERENCES

1. See, for instance, E. C. POLLARD and W. L. DAVIDSON, *Applied Nuclear Physics*, Wiley, 2nd Edn. 1951.

2. *op. cit.*, p. 96.

3. *op. cit.*, p. 106.

4. e.g. *op. cit.*, Chapter 11.

13. PROPERTIES OF THE ATOMIC NUCLEUS

1. The expression for the nuclear radius is
$$R = 1 \cdot 5 \, A^{1/3} \text{ fermi,}$$
where A is the mass number and 1 fermi $= 10^{-13}$ cm.

2. The semi-empirical formula for the mass of an atom in mass units is:
$$M(A, Z) = Z m_{\text{H}} + (A - Z) \, m_n - 0 \cdot 01507 \, A + 0 \cdot 014 \, A^{2/3}$$
$$+ 0 \cdot 000627 \, \frac{Z^2}{A^{1/3}} + 0 \cdot 0207 \, \frac{(A - 2Z)^2}{A} + \delta(A, Z),$$

where m_H and m_n are the masses of the hydrogen atom and the neutron in MU
$$\delta(A, Z) = \begin{cases} -0 \cdot 036 \, A^{-3/4} & (A \text{ even}, Z \text{ even}), \\ 0 & (A \text{ odd}, Z \text{ either odd or even}), \\ +0 \cdot 036 \, A^{-3/4} & (A \text{ even}, Z \text{ odd}). \end{cases}$$

3. The total angular momentum of an atom is
$$\mathbf{F} = \mathbf{J} + \mathbf{I},$$

where $\mathbf{J}$ is the total angular momentum of the electronic shell; $\mathbf{I}$ is the angular momentum (spin) of the nucleus.

The selection rule for the quantum number F for allowed transitions is:
$$\Delta F = 0, \ \pm 1,$$
$$F = 0 \nrightarrow F = 0.$$

4. The magnetic moment of a nucleus is:
$$\mu = g \mu_n \sqrt{I(I + 1)},$$

where g is the gyromagnetic ratio; μ_n is the nuclear magneton.

The value of the maximum projection of the vector μ on the direction of the magnetic field, usually given in the tables, is
$$\mu_{\text{H}} = g \mu_n I.$$

RADIUS AND MASS OF A NUCLEUS. BINDING ENERGY

13.1. Which of the following nuclei are isotopes, isobars, isotones, mirror nuclei:[1] B^{12}, C^{14}, N^{14}, O^{14}, and O^{16}? What nuclei are said to be isomers?

13.2. From the expression for the nuclear radius find the density of nuclear matter.

13.3. List and describe briefly all the methods used to determine nuclear radii.

13.4. From the expression for the nuclear radius estimate what energy electrons must have to produce a clearly defined diffraction pattern when scattered on nuclei of He^4 and of uranium.

13.5. For a uniform distribution of protons in a spherical nucleus their electrostatic interaction energy is

$$\frac{3}{5} \frac{e^2 Z(Z-1)}{R},$$

where Z is the atomic number and R the nuclear radius. Assume that the difference in binding energy between the mirror nuclei B^{11} and C^{11}, C^{13} and N^{13}, N^{15} and O^{15} is due only to the difference in their electrostatic energies and calculate the radii of these nuclei.

13.6. What is the meaning of each of the terms in the semi-empirical mass formula? What is the expression for the total binding energy of a nucleus?

13.7. Calculate the atomic masses of Cl^{37} and Ca^{40} from the semi-empirical mass formula. Compare the results obtained with those given in the tables.

13.8. Use the semi-empirical mass formula to determine the atomic number Z of the beta-stable nucleus for each of the following mass numbers: 23, 51, 89, 114.

13.9. Use the semi-empirical mass formula to find the energy of the alpha particle emitted by the U^{235} nucleus.

13.10. (a) Write down the expressions representing the transformations of the nucleons in the β^- and β^+ decay of nuclei.

(b) When beta active nuclei are produced by bombarding stable nuclei A with alpha particles they emit either β^- or β^+ particles, depending on the type of the original reaction: $A(\alpha, p)A' \rightarrow \beta^-$, $A(\alpha, n)A'' \rightarrow \beta^+$. What type of β-radiation would you expect to find from the nuclei A' and A''?

13.11. From the semi-empirical formula find the value of Z^2/A for which the fission of a nucleus with even Z and A into two equal parts becomes energetically probable (neglect the $\delta(A, Z)$ correction factor). Where in the periodic system does one find such elements?

13.12. As was shown by Frenkel and by Bohr and Wheeler, a nucleus is completely unstable with respect to fission into two equal fragments when the ratio of its electrostatic and surface energies becomes equal to 2.

(a) Find the value Z^2/A for such a nucleus.

(b) Compare the Z^2/A values for the last elements in the periodic table with the value so obtained; explain why the nuclei of these elements are fissile.

13.13. What is meant by the expression "charge symmetry of nuclear forces"? Sketch the form of the potential energy of interaction of the following three pairs of nucleons: n–n, p–p, and p–p.

13.14. Represent the potential energy of interaction of nucleons in a deuteron in the form of a rectangular spherical well (Fig. 24) of depth U_0 and radius R, and find

(a) the form of the wave function $\psi(r)$ of the ground state of the deuteron, assuming that in this state it is spherically symmetric;

(b) the relation between U_0 and R; assuming $R = 2 \cdot 82$ fermi and $E = 2 \cdot 23$ MeV, find the numerical value of U_0.

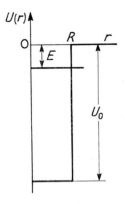

FIG. 24

13.15. From the deuteron model shown on Fig. 24

(a) find the most probable distance between the neutron and the proton in the ground state, assuming that $U_0 = 21$ MeV, and that the binding energy is $E = 2 \cdot 23$ MeV;

(b) represent graphically the wave function of the deuteron $\psi(r)$ and how the probability $W(r)$ depends on the relative distance of the nucleons in this state (assume $R = 2 \cdot 82$ fermi).

SPIN AND MAGNETIC MOMENT OF A NUCLEUS

13.16. For which class of nuclei must the Pauli principle be applied for determining the states of molecules or condensed systems?

13.17. Give an explanation for the fine and hyperfine structures of spectral lines.

13.18. (a) Under what condition is the number of components in the hyperfine structure of an atomic term determined by the nuclear spin I?

(b) Into how many hyperfine structure components will the terms describing the ground states of the following atoms be split:

$$H^3(^2S_{1/2}, I = \tfrac{1}{2}), \quad Li^6(^2S_{1/2}, I = 1), \quad Be^9(^1S_0, I = \tfrac{1}{2}),$$

$$N^{14}(^4S_{1/2}, I = 1), \quad N^{15}(^4S_{3/2}, I = \tfrac{1}{2}) \quad \text{and} \quad Cl^{35}(^2P_{3/2}, I = \tfrac{3}{2})?$$

13.19. What is the angular momentum of the nucleus Co^{59}, assuming that its normal atomic term $^4F_{9/2}$ splits into 8 components.

13.20. Calculate the statistical weights (the degree of degeneracy) of the terms $^2P_{1/2}$ and $^2D_{3/2}$ of the Al^{27} atom, which has a nuclear spin of $5/2$. Does the ratio of the statistical weights of these terms depend upon the nuclear spin I?

13.21. The intensity ratio of the components in the hyperfine splitting of the spectral line arising in the transition $^2P_{1/2} \rightarrow {}^2S_{1/2}$ in the atoms Li^7, Na^{23} and K^{39} is on the average equal to 0·6. Taking into account that the splitting of the term $^2P_{1/2}$ is negligibly small, determine the nuclear spin I of these atoms. Why is the splitting of the P term considerably smaller than the splitting of the S term?

13.22. Beams of $Be^9(^1S_0)$ and $C^{13}(^3P_0)$ atoms pass through a strong, sharply inhomogeneous magnetic field, (the Stern–Gerlach

4 a*

method). As a result of this the beams are split respectively into 4 and 2 components. Determine the nuclear spins of Be^9 and C^{13}.

13.23. In the original experiments of Rabi a beam of Na^{23} atoms (in the $^2S_{1/2}$ state) was successively passed, first through a sharply inhomogeneous strong field H_1, and then through an extended sharply inhomogeneous weak field H_2 (Fig. 25). As a result the beam was split into 8 components. Determine the nuclear spin of Na^{23}.

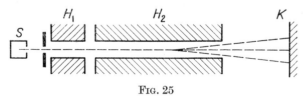

FIG. 25

13.24. Find the projection of the magnetic moment of the neutron μ_H, if the resonance frequency of the variable magnetic field in the Rabi experiment (the method of magnetic resonance) is found to be 26×10^6 c/s when the constant magnetic field is $H = 8900$ oe. Calculate also μ, the magnetic moment of the neutron.

13.25. A beam of Mg^{25} atoms in the $^1S_0$ ground state is made to pass through a sequence of magnetic fields (the magnetic resonance method) as in the Rabi experiments. With a of field strength $H = 13\cdot5$ koe the resonance frequency is found to be $3\cdot5 \times 10^6$ c/s. Determine the gyromagnetic ratio and the nuclear spin of Mg^{25}, given also that the maximum projection of the atomic magnetic moment in this state is $\mu_H = 0\cdot85$ nuclear magnetons.

12.26. Draw the vector model of a nucleon in a nucleus. Knowing that the spin and orbital gyromagnetic factors of a nucleon (g_s and g_l) are not equal, explain the presence of the gyromagnetic factor in the expression

$$\mu = g_j \mu_R \sqrt{j(j+1)}.$$

13.27. From the relation $\mu = g_s \mathbf{s} + g_l \mathbf{l}$ derive an expression for the gyromagnetic factor g_j of a nucleon. Here g_s and g_l are the gyromagnetic factors characteristic of the spin (s) and the orbital (l) motion in the nucleus.

13.28. From the expression for the gyromagnetic factor of a nucleus (see the solution of the preceding problem) calculate the magnetic moment of a proton ($g_s = 5 \cdot 58$, $g_l = 1$) and neutron ($g_s = -3 \cdot 82$, $g_l = 0$) in the following states: $s_{1/2}$, $p_{1/2}$ and $p_{3/2}$.

13.29. Estimate the value of the projection of the magnetic moment of a deuteron whose nucleons are in the s state ($l = 0$), given that the gyromagnetic factor of a proton is $g_s = 5 \cdot 58$ and that of a neutron is $g_s = -3 \cdot 82$.

13.30. Assume that the size of a nucleus is of the order of 10^{-12} cm and use the indeterminacy relations to show that an electron cannot be present in a nucleus as an independent elementary particle bound only by the coulomb force. Carry out the proof for light nuclei ($Z \approx 10$).

REFERENCES

1. See, for instance, I. KAPLAN, *Nuclear Physics*, Addison-Wesley, 1955.
2. *op. cit.*, p. 425.

14. ELEMENTARY PARTICLES

1. The threshold kinetic energy of a bombarding particle m necessary to produce a particle m' in a collision with a nucleus M at rest is

$$E_{\text{thr}} = \frac{(m' + \sum M_i')^2 - (m + M)^2}{2M} c^2,$$

Here $\sum M_i$ is the sum of the rest masses of all the particles except m' after the collision, m and M are the rest masses of the corresponding particles after the collision and c is the velocity of light.

When the kinetic energy of the incident particle has the threshold value, the relative velocity of the particles produced in the collision is zero.

2. The relations between the lengths (l, l_0) and the time intervals (τ, τ_0) in inertial frames of reference moving relative to each other with a velocity v are:

$$l = l_0 \sqrt{1 - \beta^2},$$

$$\tau = \tau_0 / \sqrt{1 - \beta^2},$$

where l_0 and τ_0 refer to the "proper" system of coordinates and $\beta = v/c$.

14.1. An 0·1 MeV K^+-meson is elastically scattered by a proton at rest. Determine the kinetic energy of the two particles after the collision, if the angle between the recoil direction of the proton and the original direction of motion of the meson is $\varphi = 45°$.

14.2. The scattering of a certain non-relativistic elementary particle with an initial kinetic energy $E = 0·5$ MeV is observed in a Wilson cloud chamber, placed in a uniform magnetic field $H = 4400$ oe. The radii of curvature of the paths of the recoil proton and of the scattered particle are both equal to $\varrho = 7·4$ cm. Identify the scattered particle by determining its mass.

14.3. Show that for the elastic central collision of a non-relativistic particle m_1 with a particle m_2 at rest (the charges of the two particles have the same sign) the following equality holds at the moment of closest approach:

$$\frac{\mu v^2}{2} = \frac{e_1 e_2}{r_{\min}} .$$

Here μ is the reduced mass of the particles, e_1 and e_2 their charges, $r_{\min}$ their distance of closest approach and v the velocity of the moving particle.

14.4. What is the minimum distance to which a μ^+-meson moving with a velocity $v = 5 \times 10^8$ cm/sec will approach a proton in an elastic collision, if the meson is deflected by an angle $\vartheta = 90°$ from its original direction of motion? For simplicity consider the proton to be at rest during the collision.

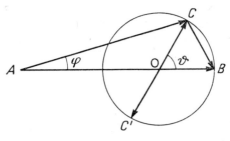

FIG. 26

14.5. The vector diagram for the elastic collision of a non-relativistic particle of mass M and momentum **AB** with a particle of mass $m < M$ at rest is shown in Fig. 26. **AC** and **CB** are the momenta of the particles M and m in the laboratory system after the collision, **OC** and **OC'** the momenta of the same particles in the centre of mass system.

(a) Explain this diagram.

(b) Draw similar diagrams for the cases when $M = m$ and $M < m$.

14.6. From the vector diagram shown in Fig. 26 determine the maximum possible value of the angle $\varphi_{\max}$ (in the laboratory system) through which a meson is scattered in an elastic collision with a free electron originally at rest. Both particles are non-relativistic.

14.7. A relativistic K^--meson of energy E passes an electron at rest with negligible change in direction, the electron acquiring the momentum p perpendicular to the direction of motion of the meson.

(a) Derive an expression for the impact parameter of the K^--meson.

(b) Calculate the value of ϱ, assuming $E = 494$ MeV and $p = 3 \times 10^{-18}$ g cm/sec.

14.8. Use the results of the preceding problem[1] to find the energy distribution of non-relativistic recoil electrons when fast charged mesons pass through matter. The binding energies of the electrons in atoms can be neglected.

14.9. In what cases of annihilation of electron–positron pairs are either one or two γ-quanta emitted?

14.10. (a) Can a γ-quantum with an energy of $2m_0c^2$ give rise to a particle–antiparticle pair (m_0 is the rest mass of the particles)?

(b) Find an expression for the minimum (threshold) energy that a γ-quantum must have to create a pair of particles in the field of a stationary nucleus of mass M.

14.11. Find the difference in threshold energies of the γ-quanta necessary for the creation of electron–positron pairs in the fields of the hydrogen atoms H^1 and H^2.

14.12. The radii of curvature of an electron–positron pair created by a γ-quantum in the field of a heavy nucleus, are each equal to 3 cm in a magnetic field of 500 oe. Find the wavelength of the γ-quantum. Neglect the recoil of the nucleus.

14.13. The mean life of charged π-mesons with a kinetic energy $E = 7m_0c^2$ (m_0 is the rest mass of the meson) in the laboratory system is $\tau = 1\cdot76 \times 10^{-5}$ sec. Find the mean lifetime of these mesons in their rest frame.

14.14. Show in general that the rest mass of a particle capable of any kind of decay is greater than the sum of the rest masses of the resulting particles.

14.15. Calculate the total kinetic energy of the particles created in the decay of a neutron at rest.

14.16. What will be the distribution of the kinetic energies of the particles produced in the decay of stopped a π^+-meson? See the decay scheme in the tables of the Appendix.

14.17. Determine the velocity of a neutron created in the decay of a stopped sigma particle Σ^-.

14.18. Derive an expression for the threshold kinetic energy E_{thr} of an incident particle m necessary for the creation of a meson m' on a nucleus of mass M at rest according to the scheme $m + M \to m' + M'$. Here m, M, M' and m' are the rest masses of the particles.

14.19. One of the two particles created when protons are bombarded by protons is a π^+-meson. Write down the corresponding reaction and calculate the threshold kinetic energy necessary for the creation of such a meson.

14.20. Determine the threshold kinetic energy that an incident particle (electron, proton) must have to create a pair in a collision with a similar particle at rest ($m + m \to \tilde{m} + m + 2m$).

14.21. Find the total kinetic energy of the products of the reaction $\gamma + p \to n + \pi^+$, when the gamma quantum has threshold energy and the proton is originally at rest.

14.22. What must be the value of the kinetic energy of a K^0-meson for one of the two π^0-mesons into which it can decay to be at rest?

14.23. A 100 MeV K^0-meson decays in flight into two π^0-mesons moving symmetrically relative to the direction of motion of the K^0-meson. Determine the angle φ between the directions of motion of the π^0-mesons.

14.24. In a bubble chamber in a 7500 oe magnetic field a Λ^0-particle is observed to decay into a proton and a π-meson, which fly apart at an angle of $\varphi = 60°$ to each other (Fig. 27). The radii of curvature of the proton and the meson in this case are respectively 25 and 50 cm. Find the value of the momentum and the direction of motion of the Λ^0-particle (for example, the angle between the momenta p_λ and p_p).

FIG. 27

14.25. A cascade Ξ-hyperon with 200 MeV of kinetic energy decays in flight into $\Lambda^0 + \pi^-$ while passing through a nuclear photo emulsion. The π^--meson flies off at right angles to the direction of motion of the Ξ-hyperon. Find the angle at which the Λ^0-particles fly off.

REFERENCE

1. See, for instance, *Methods of Experimental Physics* (Editor: L. Marton). Vol. 5 *Nuclear Physics*, edited by L. C. L. Yuan and C. S. Wu. Academic Press 1961. Part A, p. 4.

15. EXPERIMENTAL METHODS
OF ATOMIC PHYSICS

1. Stokes' law:

$$F = 6\pi\eta r v,$$

here F is the frictional force acting on a spherical particle of radius r that moves with a velocity v through a viscous medium of viscosity η.

2. The force acting on a charge e in an electromagnetic field is:

$$\mathbf{F} = e\mathbf{E} + \frac{e}{c}[\mathbf{vH}],$$

where $\mathbf{v}$ is the velocity of the particle, $\mathbf{E}$ the electric field strength, $\mathbf{H}$ the magnetic field strength and c the velocity of light.

3. The radius of the trajectory of a charged particle in a magnetic field of strength H is:

$$\varrho = \frac{mvc}{eH},$$

where e and m are the charge and the mass of the particle respectively and v is its velocity.

4. The period of revolution of a charged particle in a homogeneous magnetic field is:

$$T = \frac{2\pi mc}{eH},$$

where e and m are the charge and the mass of the particle.

5. The condition for the motion of an electron in the stable orbit in a betatron ("the betatron condition") is expressed by:

$$H_0 = \tfrac{1}{2}\overline{H},$$

where H_0 is the magnetic field strength for the orbit, and $\overline{H}$ the average field strength inside the orbit.

6. The relativistic relation between the total energy of a particle E and its momentum p is:

$$E^2 = p^2c^2 + m_0^2 c^4,$$

where m_0 is the rest mass of the particle.

One should bear in mind that in the following problems the term "particle energy" E refers to the kinetic energy, which is the difference between its total energy and its rest energy:

$$E = E - m_0 c^2.$$

DETERMINATION OF e AND e/m FOR CHARGED PARTICLES

CHARGED PARTICLE ANALYZERS

15.1. A drop of water $5\,\mu$ in diameter moves with a constant velocity in the field of a vertical plate condenser. The electric field intensity in the condenser is $E = 1410$ V/cm. The angle between the direction of motion of the drop and the plates is $\alpha = 10°$. Determine the number of elementary charges carried by the drop. Neglect the density of the medium.

15.2. Strictly speaking, Stokes' law is applicable only when the radius r of the drop is considerably larger than the mean free path (λ) of the molecules of the medium. For very small droplets one must introduce into the expression for the Stokes' law a factor

$$\frac{1}{1 + A\dfrac{\lambda}{r}},$$

where $A = 1.25$ at n.t.p. Taking this into account:

(a) Obtain an improved formula for the charge on a droplet, given that if in a horizontal plane condenser the direction of the field E is reversed, the velocity of the drop changes from v_1 to v_2.

(b) Estimate the relative error in determining the charge on a droplet 10^{-3} mm in diameter when the ordinary expression is used for the Stokes' law. It is known that at n.t.p. $\lambda = 7 \times 10^{-6}$ cm.

15.3. Show that the small deviation of a charged particle from the initial direction of motion in a transverse, homogeneous magnetic field is proportional to e/mv and in a transverse homogeneous electric field proportional to e/mv^2, where e is the charge, m the mass and v the velocity of the particle.

15.4. A charged 0.12 MeV meson enters into a transverse uniform magnetic field of strength 100 oe. Determine the mass of the meson if its deflection from the original direction of motion amounts to 3 mm for a trajectory 10 cm long.

15.5. A beam of alpha particles accelerated by a potential difference $U = 10\,\mathrm{kV}$, enters a transverse homogeneous magnetic field 5 cm long. Given the charge and the mass of the alpha particle, determine for what strength of the magnetic field the deviation on a screen placed 25 cm away from the point where the beam leaves the field will be 1·5 cm.

15.6. One of the most exact methods used to determine the specific charge of an electron is the method of two condensers. The method is based on letting a narrow beam of electrons, accelerated by a voltage U, pass successively through the transverse electric fields of two small condensers a distance L from each other (Fig. 28). In both condensers the same generator G sets up oscillating fields synchronized in phase. By a suitable change of the frequency of the generator the beam of electrons passes through both condensers without changing its direction.

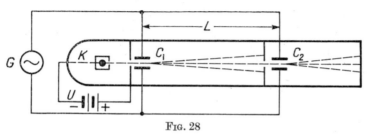

Fig. 28

(a) Derive the conditions under which this can be realized and obtain an expression for the ratio e/m for an electron.

(b) If $U = 1\,\mathrm{kV}$ and $L = 20$ cm, what is the minimum frequency of the generator necessary to obtain this condition?

15.7. Show that a transverse homogeneous magnetic field can serve as an analyser of charged particles according to momenta and of monoenergetic particles according to their masses. All particles are assumed to have the same charge.

15.8. In a Dempster mass-spectrometer a weakly diverging monoenergetic beam of singly ionized Be^6 and Be^7 is focused by a transverse homogeneous magnetic field $H = 5000$ oe, after a rotation through 180°.

(a) Find the value of the linear divergence of the beams at the focal point, given that the energy of the ions corresponds to an accelerating potential of $U = 5\,\mathrm{kV}$.

(b) Find the dispersion of the apparatus, i.e. the quantity $\Delta\chi/\Delta M$ at the focus, where $\Delta\chi$ is the distance between neighbouring beams whose masses (in atomic mass units) differ by ΔM.

15.9. In physical experiments a mass spectrometer (Fig. 29) is widely used, whose analyzer consists of a transverse, radially symmetric magnetic field which focuses the charged particles after a rotation through an angle of $\pi\sqrt{2}$ radians (255°). The ion source and the collector slit are at equal distances r_0 from the centre of the field. The apparatus has a dispersion of

$$\frac{\Delta r}{\Delta p} = 4\frac{r_0}{p},$$

where Δr is the distance at the focus between neighbouring beams of particles, whose momenta differ by Δp, and p is the average momentum of the particles. Determine whether by means of this

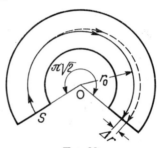

Fig. 29

mass-spectrometer one can separate the isotopes of uranium U^{234}, U^{235} and U^{238}, if $r_0 = 10$ cm and the width of each beam at the focusing point is 1 mm. The source is assumed to emit monoenergetic ions.

15.10. In a Wilson cloud chamber placed in a homogeneous magnetic field of 400 oe, the radius of curvature at the beginning of a proton trajectory is 12 cm. The initial proton velocity is $v = 4.6 \times 10^7$ cm/sec. Determine e/m for the proton.

15.11. A parallel beam of charged particles, 2 cm² in cross-section, enters an ionization chamber. Under the conditions of the experiment each particle creates 20 pairs of ions per cm of path. Calculate the current density of these particles, given that the path length of the beam in the chamber is 5 cm and the saturation current through the ionization chamber is 5×10^{-10} amp.

15.12. A Geiger–Müller counter with a dead time of 2×10^{-4} sec registers 500 pulses per sec. Find the intensity of the incoming beam of particles n_0 and the corresponding relative error of counting.

15.13. It has been shown theoretically that the standard deviation of a single measurement of a phenomenon statistical in character is approximately equal to $\sqrt{N}$, where N is the number of events registered in the measurement. Estimate the number of pulses one should register with a counter so that the relative error of measurement is 1 per cent.

15.14. Show that if the number of pulses due to background radiation is equal to the number of pulses from the source being investigated, then to obtain a given precision of measurement one should register 6 times more pulses than if there were no background.

Hint: In observing two independent events the standard deviation of the measurement is

$$\Delta = \sqrt{\Delta_1^2 + \Delta_2^2},$$

where Δ_1 and Δ_2 are the standard deviations of the independent measurements.

CHARGED PARTICLE ACCELERATORS

15.15. Find the velocity acquired by protons in a Van de Graaff generator, given that the distance between the center of the charged sphere of diameter $d = 2$ m and the base of the generator is $L = 10$ m, and that the critical electric field strength on the surface of the sphere is $E = 80$ kV/cm. The particles are accelerated in a vertical discharge tube placed between the sphere and the base of the generator. For simplicity consider that the sphere is uniformly charged and that the base is a conducting plane.

15.16. Describe briefly the two methods for exciting the electromagnetic waves between the sections of a linear accelerator illustrated in (Fig. 30) of the (a) old and (b) new type.

15.17. A travelling wave linear accelerator consists of a cylindrical loaded wave guide, along which is propagated an electromagnetic

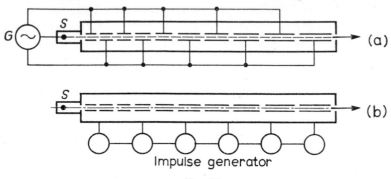

FIG. 30

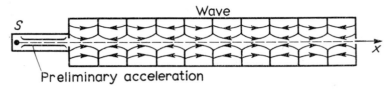

Preliminary acceleration

FIG. 31

wave with an axial component E_x (Fig. 31). By disposing the annular diaphragms in a given way one obtains an increase of phase velocity of the wave down the wave guide such that at all times the accelerated particle is approximately coincident with the same phase of the wave.

(a) Find the energy of the electrons at the terminal of an accelerator 67 m in length, if E_x is 150 kV/cm and the initial electron energy is 4 MeV.

(b) From the relativistic equation for the motion of a particle find an expression for the change of the wave phase velocity along the wave guide.

15.18. (a) Show that for small energies the period of revolution of a charged particle in a homogeneous magnetic field does not depend upon the energy itself. Define "small energies" in this case.

(b) Determine the radius of curvature of the trajectory and the period of revolution of an electron, a proton and an alpha particle in a homogeneous magnetic field of strength $H = 1$ koe, assuming that the energy of each particle is 1 per cent of its rest energy.

15.19. Neglecting the relativistic increase of particle mass with velocity calculate to what energy one can accelerate a proton, a deuteron and an alpha particle in a cyclotron (Fig. 32) in which a homogeneous magnetic field of strength $H = 10$ koe extends to a radius of $\varrho = 30$ cm?

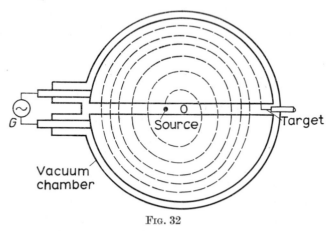

FIG. 32

15.20. Determine the frequency of a generator feeding a cyclotron that accelerates deuterons up to $E = 2$ MeV when the maximum radius of curvature of the trajectory of the particle is $\varrho = 49$ cm.

15.21. A beam of alpha particles accelerated in a cyclotron is allowed to pass into air through an aluminium window of mass thickness 5 mg/cm². The maximum radius of curvature of the alpha particles in the cyclotron is 40 cm, and the magnetic field strength is 13,000 oe. Find the range of the beam in the air.

Hint. The range of an alpha particle in a substance of mass number A and density ϱ is given by the expression

$$L = 3 \cdot 2 \times 10^{-4} \frac{\sqrt{A}}{\varrho} R \quad \text{cm},$$

where R is its range in the air.

15.22. Show that in the cyclic acceleration of particles in a magnetic field the period of revolution of a particle increases with energy on account of the relativistic effect. Calculate the periods of revolution of electrons and of protons in a magnetic field of 10 koe at the following energies: 1 MeV, 100 MeV and 10,000 MeV.

15.23. A cyclotron is not suitable for accelerating electrons since their orbiting period increases rapidly with the increase of energy so that resonance is destroyed. This effect, however, can be corrected, if the change of the orbiting period of the electron ΔT is made equal to a multiple of the period of the accelerating field T_0. An accelerator working on this principle is called a microtron. How many times should an electron pass through the accelerating interval of a microtron to acquire an energy $E = 4 \cdot 6$ MeV, if $\Delta T = T_0$, the magnetic field intensity is $H = 10$ koe and the wavelength of the accelerating field $\lambda = 10 \cdot 7$ cm?

15.24. What is the basic difference between a synchrocyclotron and a cyclotron? Determine the modulation depth of a synchrocyclotron, i.e., the relative change in frequency of the accelerating field necessary to accelerate protons up to 200 MeV.

15.25. It is well known that a synchrocyclotron operates in pulses (usually about 100 pulses/sec). Assuming that the average current density in a proton beam is $1 \cdot 6 \times 10^{-9}$ amp/cm^2, determine:

(a) the average proton flux density in the beam;

(b) the flux of protons per pulse, when the duration of the pulse is 0·01 per cent of the whole accelerating cycle.

15.26. The magnetic flux within a stable orbit in a betatron changes at a constant rate of 2×10^9 maxwells/sec. What is the energy of the electrons accelerated over 10^6 revolutions?

15.27. Determine the maximum energy and the corresponding wavelength of gamma rays produced by abruptly stopping in matter electrons accelerated in a betatron under the following condition: during a period of acceleration of 5×10^{-4} sec the magnetic flux within the orbit of 8 cm radius increases from zero at a constant rate of $1 \cdot 5 \times 10^9$ maxwells/sec.

15.28. The magnetic field in a betatron decreases toward its edge as follows:

$$H = a\varrho^n,$$

where a is a certain constant and ϱ is the distance from the centre of the field.

(a) Show that stability of the motion of an electron in the horizontal plane is assured, provided $0 < n < 1$, in which case a small deviation from the stable orbit gives rise to a force tending to turn the electron back.

(b) Assuming that $n = 0.6$ and that the radius of the stable orbit is $\varrho_0 = 10$ cm, determine the magnitude of this force for a deviation from equilibrium of $\eta = 1$ per cent for electrons of energies $E_1 = 0.1$ MeV and $E_2 = 10$ MeV.

15.29. In cyclic accelerators the unlimited increase of energy of an electron is prevented by the loss of energy through radiation, as the electron moves in a circular orbit. L. A. Artsimovich and I. Ya. Pomeranchuk have shown that the energy lost by an electron during one revolution is $W = 88\ E^4/\varrho$ kev, where E is the energy of an electron in BeV, and ϱ is the orbit radius in meters. Hence find the value of the maximum energy that an electron can acquire in a betatron when the rate of change of magnetic field strength for an orbit of 50 cm radius is 10^3 koe/sec.

15.30. All modern accelerators with variable electric fields work on the principle of stable longitudinal motion of the accelerated particles (the self-focusing principle of V. I. Vexler and MacMillan). Explain the basic idea of this principle.

15.31. What is the basic principle of a proton–synchrotron and how does it differ from other cyclic accelerators: the cyclotron, the synchrocyclotron, the betatron and the synchrotron?

15.32. In a gigantic proton–synchrotron in the Joint Institute of Nuclear Research, a proton with an initial velocity of 9 MeV is accelerated to 10 BeV, gaining on the average an energy of 2·2 keV per turn. The length of the stable orbit (taking into account the rectilinear sections, Fig. 33) is 200 m. The acceleration time is 3·3 sec.

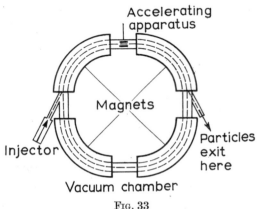

FIG. 33

(a) Determine the number of revolutions and the path length covered by protons in the whole period of acceleration.

(b) What is the average rate of increase of magnetic field strength for the circular portions of the orbit, whose radius of curvature is equal to 28 m?

(c) What is the final velocity of the protons?

15.33. One way to increase considerably the energies of colliding particles is to produce two beams of particles, each of energy E, moving against each other. Determine the magnitude of the relative energy of protons colliding under these conditions, assuming that $E = 25$ BeV.

REFERENCES

1. *op. cit.*, Chapter 11, p. 210.

2. *Experimental Nuclear Physics*, Editor: E. Segrè. Wiley, 1953. Vol. I, part V (Mass spectrometers, etc.).

3. M S. LIVINGSTON, *High Energy Accelerators*, Interscience, 1962.

Answers

ANSWERS

1.1. (a) $[\varrho] = \text{erg/cm}^3$, $[J] = [I] = \text{erg/cm}^2 \sec$;

(b) $[\varrho_\nu] = \text{erg sec/cm}^3$, $[J_\nu] = \text{erg/cm}^2$

1.2. $\Delta\Phi = \pi J \Delta\sigma\tau = 1\cdot89$ joule.

1.3. Unlike the kinds of radiation listed, black body radiation is radiation in thermal equilibrium.

1.4. Quartz is transparent to visible light, and consequently, it emits only very weakly in this portion of the spectrum.

1.5. Let E be the emissive power and A the absorptive power of the "grey" portion and I the emissive power of a black body. Then the total quantity of energy emitted by the "grey" portion consists of the emitted and the reflected energy:

$$E\Delta\sigma + (1-A)I\Delta\sigma.$$

Since by Kirchhoff's law $AI = E$, the preceding expression proves to be equal to $I\Delta\sigma$, as in the case of a black body.

1.6. For a certain arbitrary frequency ν_1 at temperature T_1 we have, from Wien's law:

$$\varrho(\nu_1, T_1) = \nu_1^3 f\left(\frac{\nu_1}{T_1}\right).$$

For a frequency ν_2, taken at temperature T_2 and satisfying the condition

$$\frac{\nu_2}{T_2} = \frac{\nu_1}{T_1},$$

we obtain

$$\varrho(\nu_1, T_1) = \left(\frac{T_1}{T_2}\right)^3 \varrho(\nu_2, T_2).$$

1.7. From the conditions $\mathrm{d}\varrho_\lambda/\mathrm{d}\lambda = 0$ and $\mathrm{d}\varrho_\nu/\mathrm{d}\nu = 0$ we have respectively:

$$5f(x) + x f'(x) = 0,$$
$$3f(x) + x f'(x) = 0,$$

where $x = cT/\lambda$.

The roots x_1 and x_2 of these two equations are not equal and consequently the wavelengths corresponding to the maxima of the functions ϱ_λ and ϱ_ν will also be different.

1.8. 5500; 8300 and 10,000°K.

1.9. About 500°C.

1.10. 875°K.

1.11.
$$T = \sqrt[4]{\frac{4(1-\eta)W}{\sigma \pi d^2}} = 2100°\,\text{K},$$

where σ is the Stefan–Boltzmann constant.

1.12. $4 \cdot 1 \times 10^{12}$ g/sec. About 10^{11} years.

1.13. Taking into account the relation between the pressure of the black body radiation and its energy density, as well as the Stefan–Boltzmann law, we have:

$$T = \sqrt[4]{\frac{3cp}{4\sigma}} = 20 \times 10^6 \,\text{deg},$$

where c is the velocity of light and σ is the Stefan–Boltzmann constant.

1.14. The gas pressure is

$$p_g = n_0 k T = 2N \frac{\varrho}{A} k T,$$

where N is Avogadro's number, and A the atomic weight of hydrogen. The factor 2 in this expression takes into account the dissociation of atoms into electrons and nuclei. The radiation pressure is

$$p_r = \frac{4}{3c} \sigma T^4,$$

where σ is the Stefan–Boltzmann constant. From the equality of the two pressures it follows that

$$T = \sqrt[3]{\frac{3\varrho kcN}{2\sigma A}} = 1 \cdot 87 \times 10^7 \,°\text{K}.$$

1.15.
$$c_v = \left(\frac{\partial \varrho}{\partial T}\right)_v = \frac{16\sigma T^3}{c} = 0 \cdot 03 \,\text{erg/deg} \cdot \text{cm}^3.$$

1.16. (a) The simplest way to calculate the entropy S is to integrate the expression

$$S = \int \frac{\mathrm{d}U + p\,\mathrm{d}v}{T}$$

over "the path" OVS (Fig. 34). As the result of this we have

$$S = \frac{16\sigma v T^3}{3c} = 2{\cdot}74 \times 10^{-7} \text{ erg/deg.}$$

(b) $$S = \frac{c_v}{3} \text{ (see problem 1.15).}$$

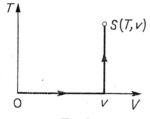

Fig. 34

1.17. $$\Delta S = \frac{4(n-1)v_0\sigma T_0^3}{3c} \approx 2 \times 10^{-4} \text{ erg/deg,}$$

where σ is the Stefan–Boltzmann constant, T_0 room temperature on the absolute scale and c the velocity of light.

1.18. The "ultraviolet catastrophe" occurs when the postulate of the equipartition of energy over all degrees of freedom of a system is applied to calculate the density of the radiation energy. Since the number of degrees of freedom of the electromagnetic field treated, via Maxwell's equations, as a system of oscillators, is infinite, the energy density obtained by using the equipartition postulate is also infinite.

1.19. $$\varrho_\lambda = \frac{8\pi hc}{\lambda^5} \frac{1}{e^{hc/kT\lambda} - 1}.$$

1.20. $$\varrho_\nu = \frac{8\pi kT}{c^3}\nu^2\,(h\nu \ll kT); \quad \varrho_\nu = \frac{8\pi h\nu^3}{c^3}e^{-h\nu/kT}\,(h\nu \gg kT).$$

1.21. $$J_{\lambda 1}/J_{\lambda 2} = 1{\cdot}15.$$

1.22. $$\Delta\lambda = 12{\cdot}4 \text{ Å.}$$

1.23.   (a) $I = \dfrac{c}{4}\varrho = \dfrac{c}{4}\displaystyle\int_{0}^{\infty} \dfrac{8\pi h\nu^3}{c^3}\dfrac{\mathrm{d}\nu}{\mathrm{e}^{h\nu/kT} - 1} \sim T^4.$

(b) $I_x = \dfrac{2\pi k^5 T^5 x^5}{h^4 c^3 (\mathrm{e}^x - 1)}, \quad \text{where} \quad x = hc/kT\lambda.$

The function I_x has a maximum for a certain value of x, and consequently

$$I_{\lambda\,\mathrm{max}} \sim T^5.$$

(c) $I \sim \displaystyle\int_{\lambda_0}^{\infty} \dfrac{\mathrm{d}\lambda}{\lambda^5 (\mathrm{e}^{hc/kT\lambda} - 1)} = \displaystyle\int_{\lambda_0}^{\infty} \dfrac{\mathrm{d}\lambda}{\lambda^5 \left(1 + \dfrac{hc}{kT\lambda} + \ldots - 1\right)} \sim T.$

1.24. $I = \dfrac{c}{4}\displaystyle\int_{0}^{\infty} \varrho_\nu\, \mathrm{d}\nu = \dfrac{13\pi k^4}{c^2 h^3} T^4.$

The coefficient of T^4 is the Stefan–Boltzmann constant,

$$\sigma = 5 \cdot 67 \times 10^{-5}\ \mathrm{erg/cm^2\ sec\ deg^4}.$$

1.25. The condition $\dfrac{\mathrm{d}\varrho_\lambda}{\mathrm{d}\lambda} = 0$ leads to the transcendental equation

$$5 - x = 5\mathrm{e}^{-x},$$

where $x = hc/kb$. The root of this equation is found graphically to be $x_0 = 4 \cdot 965$. As a result

$$b \approx 0 \cdot 2\,\dfrac{hc}{k} \approx 0 \cdot 29\ \mathrm{cm\ deg}.$$

1.26. (a) From the condition $\dfrac{\mathrm{d}\varrho_\nu}{\mathrm{d}\nu} = 0$ we find $3f(x) + x f'(x) = 0$,

where $x = \nu/T$. This equation has the root $x_0 = \nu_{\mathrm{max}}/T$, which agrees with the required expression.

(b) The maximum of the expression in Planck's law occurs when $3 - x = 3\mathrm{e}^{-x}$, where $x = h\nu/kT$. This equation can be solved graphically ($x_0 \approx 2 \cdot 82$). We get:

$$b' = 2 \cdot 82\,\dfrac{k}{h} = 5 \cdot 88 \times 10^{10}\ \mathrm{sec^{-1}\ deg^{-1}}; \quad b' \neq \dfrac{c}{b}.$$

1.27. To solve the problem we must find the roots of the equation $5 - x = 5e^{-x}$

By a graphical method we find $x_m \approx 5$, whence $\lambda_m = 4840$ Å.

1.28. The frequency ν_0 corresponds to the maximum of the derivative $d\tau_\nu/d\nu$, which occurs for $d^2\tau_\nu/d\nu^2 = 0$. This condition leads to the transcendental equation

$$e^x(x^2 - 6x + 6) + 6e^{-x} + x^2 + 6x = 12,$$

where $x = h\nu/kT$. The roots of this equation are found graphically to be: $x_1 \approx 0 \cdot 97$, $x_2 \approx 4 \cdot 61$ (the root $x_3 = 0$ has no physical meaning within the conditions of the problem). We then determine to which of the two roots corresponds the larger absolute value of the derivative

$$\frac{d}{dx} J_x, \text{ or of } \frac{d}{d\nu} J_\nu.$$

Thus we get

$$\nu_0 \approx 0 \cdot 97 \frac{kT}{h}.$$

1.29. $\qquad h = \sqrt[3]{\dfrac{13\pi\, k^4\, T^4}{c^2\, I}} = 6 \cdot 6 \times 10^{-27} \text{ erg} \cdot \text{sec}.$

1.30. $\varrho = 8\pi \dfrac{k^4\, T^4}{h^3\, c^3} (\alpha^3 + 3\alpha^2 + 6\alpha + 6)\, e^{-\alpha} = 1 \cdot 284 \times 10^{-4} \text{ erg/cm}^3.$

Here $\qquad\qquad\qquad \alpha = h\, c/k\, T\, \lambda_0.$

1.31. From the condition

$$\frac{d}{dT}\left(\frac{\int_{\lambda_1}^{\lambda_2} J_\lambda\, d\lambda}{\int_0^\infty J_\lambda\, d\lambda}\right) = 0,$$

after substituting

$$J_\lambda = \frac{a}{\lambda^5}\, \frac{1}{e^{b/\lambda T} - 1}, \quad \text{where} \quad b = h\, c/k,$$

and after introducing the new variable $x = \lambda T$ we obtain

$$\frac{d}{dT} \int_{\lambda_1 T}^{\lambda_2 T} \frac{dx}{x^5(e^{b/x} - 1)} = 0.$$

Differentiating this integral with respect to the parameter, we obtain the following transcendental equation in T:

$$\lambda_1^4 (e^{b/\lambda_1 T} - 1) = \lambda_2^4 (e^{b/\lambda_2 T} - 1).$$

It can be solved graphically, for example by taking the function

$$x(T) = \left(\frac{\lambda_2}{\lambda_1}\right)^4 \frac{e^{b/\lambda_2 T} - 1}{e^{b/\lambda_1 T} - 1}$$

and then determining the value of T corresponding to $x = 1$. In this way we find $T \approx 6800°K$.

1.32. Increases by k^3 times, i.e., by 8 times for $k = 2$.

1.33.

$$n = 8\pi \left(\frac{kT}{hc}\right)^3 \int_0^\infty \frac{x^3 \, dx}{e^x - 1} \approx 19 \cdot 24\, \pi \left(\frac{kT}{hc}\right)^3 = 4 \cdot 14 \times 10^8 \text{ quanta cm}^3$$

1.34.
$$\bar{E} = \frac{\displaystyle\int_0^\infty h\,\nu\, n_\nu \, d\nu}{\displaystyle\int_0^\infty n_\nu \, d\nu} = 2 \cdot 70\, k\, T = 0 \cdot 23 \text{ eV}.$$

1.35. From the conditions

$$\frac{d\varrho_\nu}{d\nu} = 0 \text{ and } \frac{dn_\nu}{d\nu} = 0$$

we find respectively

$$3 - x = 3e^{-x},$$
$$2 - x = 2e^{-x},$$

where $x = h\,\nu/k\,T$. The roots of the two equations are evidently not equal, and consequently the frequencies corresponding to the maxima of the functions ϱ_ν and n_ν are different.

1.36.
$$\bar{\nu} = \frac{\displaystyle\int_0^\infty \nu \, dn_\nu}{\displaystyle\int_0^\infty dn_\nu} = \frac{3T}{a} = 3 \cdot 56 \times 10^{14} \text{ sec}^{-1}.$$

Here dn_ν is the number of quanta in the spectral interval

$$\nu, \ \nu + d\nu.$$

1.37.
$$\bar{E} = \frac{\sum\limits_{n=0}^{\infty} nh\nu\, \mathrm{e}^{-nh\nu/\theta}}{\sum\limits_{n=0}^{\infty} \mathrm{e}^{-nh\nu/\theta}},$$

where $\theta = kT$. To calculate this expression we note that the numerator can be represented as the derivative of the denominator. Hence

$$\bar{E} = \theta^2 \frac{\partial}{\partial\theta} \ln \sum_{n=0}^{\infty} \mathrm{e}^{-nh\nu/\theta} = \theta^2 \frac{\partial}{\partial\theta} \ln (\mathrm{e}^{h\nu/\theta} - 1) = \frac{h\nu}{\mathrm{e}^{h\nu/kT} - 1}.$$

1.38. (a)

$$\bar{E} = \frac{h\nu}{\mathrm{e}^{h\nu/kT} - 1} = \frac{h\nu}{1 + \dfrac{h\nu}{kT} + \ldots - 1} \approx kT, \quad T \gg h\nu/k.$$

(b) The functions $\bar{E}_\nu(T)$ and $\bar{E}_T(\nu)$ are represented graphically in Fig. 35.

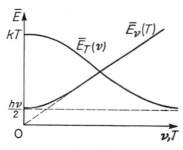

Fɪɢ. 35

2.1. $\qquad$ $0 \cdot 0242$ Å, $2 \cdot 73 \times 10^{-17}$ g · cm/sec.

2.2. $\qquad$ (a) $960°$ K; (b) $1 \cdot 6 \times 10^{4°}$K.

2.3. $\qquad T = \dfrac{\pi h^2}{8 m k \lambda^2} = 745°$K

(m is the mass of the neutron, k is Boltzmann's constant).

2.4. $\quad E = \dfrac{h c}{b \sin \varphi} = 2 \cdot 6$ eV, $\quad p = 1 \cdot 39 \times 10^{-22}$ g · cm/sec.

2.5. $\qquad \dfrac{\Delta E}{E} = \dfrac{1}{k N} = 0 \cdot 005 \%.$

2.6. Apart from a certain numerical coefficient, which depends upon the configuration and the properties of the reflecting surface and also upon the angle of incidence of light, the pressure of the flux is equal to

$$p \sim \int \frac{h}{\lambda} \, \mathrm{d} N_\nu,$$

where

$$\mathrm{d} N_\nu = \frac{J_\nu \, \mathrm{d} \nu}{h \nu}$$

is the number of quanta in the spectral interval from ν to $\nu + \mathrm{d}\nu$ that cross 1 cm² in unit time. Thus

$$p \sim \int_{\nu_1}^{\nu_2} \frac{J_\nu \, \mathrm{d} \nu}{c} = \frac{J}{c},$$

which is the required result.

2.7. $\quad p = p_{\text{inc}} + p_{\text{ref}} = \dfrac{J}{c} + \int \dfrac{h \nu}{c} \cos \vartheta \, \dfrac{J_\nu \, \mathrm{d} \nu}{h \nu} \, \dfrac{\mathrm{d}\omega}{2\pi}$

$$= \frac{3 J}{2 c} = 2 \cdot 44 \times 10^{-5} \text{ d/cm}^2.$$

2.8.
$$\varphi = \frac{W\,r}{c\,D} = 4{\cdot}8°,$$

where c is the velocity of light.

2.9. The number of quanta falling in time $\mathrm{d}t$ on a unit surface S in a given direction ϑ (Fig. 36) is

$$\mathrm{d}n_\nu\, c \cos\vartheta\,\frac{\mathrm{d}\omega}{4\pi}\,\mathrm{d}t,$$

where $\mathrm{d}n_\nu$ is the number quanta of frequency between ν and $\nu + \mathrm{d}\nu$ per unit volume

$$\left(\mathrm{d}n_\nu = \frac{\varrho_\nu\,\mathrm{d}\nu}{h\,\nu}\right) \quad \text{and} \quad \mathrm{d}\omega/4\pi$$

is the fraction of quanta with a given direction of propagation. Multiplying this last expression by p_n, the normal momentum component of each photon, and integrating over all frequencies and angles we find the total pressure force to be:

$$p = 2\int p_n\,\mathrm{d}n_\nu\, c \cos\vartheta\,\frac{\mathrm{d}\omega}{4\pi} = \frac{1}{3}\varrho\,.$$

The factor of 2 in front of the integral takes into account that, at equilibrium, for every incident quantum there is an equal quantum emitted in the opposite direction.

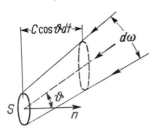

Fig. 36

2.10. Integrating the expression

$$h\,\mathrm{d}\nu = -\,\gamma\,\frac{m_\varphi\,M}{r^2}\,\mathrm{d}r,$$

where γ is the gravitational constant, and m_Φ the mass of the photon ($h\,\nu/c^2$) we have

$$\ln\frac{\nu}{\nu_0} = -\gamma\frac{M}{c^2\,R}.$$

Hence, more precisely, we have

$$\frac{\Delta\lambda}{\lambda_0} = \gamma\frac{M}{c^2\,R} = 2{\cdot}1 \times 10^{-6}.$$

2.11. There is no displacement when the star is moving toward the earth. In this case the displacement of the lines caused by the gravitational attraction of photons by the star is compensated by the Doppler effect. Hence

$$v_r = \frac{2\gamma\,M}{c\,D},$$

where γ is the gravitational constant and c the velocity of light.

2.12. We write out the laws of conservation of energy and momentum for the case when a photon is emitted by a moving particle

$$E = E' + E_\varphi,$$
$$\mathbf{P} = \mathbf{P}' + \mathbf{p}_\varphi.$$

Here E, E' and $\mathbf{P}$, $\mathbf{P}'$ are the energy and the momentum of the relativistic particle before and after emitting a photon of energy E_φ and momentum $\mathbf{p}_\varphi$ (Fig. 37).

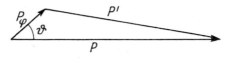

FIG. 37

Squaring the two expressions and simplifying, we obtain after appropriate transformations

$$\cos\vartheta = \frac{c}{v\,n}\left(1 + \frac{h\,\nu\,(n^2-1)}{2E}\right).$$

Since $h\,\nu \ll E$, we have with great accuracy

$$\cos\vartheta = \frac{c}{v\,n},$$

whence it is evident at once that we must have $v > c/n$

2.13. (a)

$$E_k = E - m_0 c^2 = m_0 c^2 \left(\frac{n}{\sqrt{n^2 - 1}} - 1 \right) = \begin{cases} 143 \text{ keV} & \text{electron} \\ 260 \text{ MeV} & \text{proton} \end{cases}$$

(b) $$m_0 \approx 207 \, m_e \, (\mu\text{-meson}).$$

2.14. During the time

$$t = \frac{h c}{J \lambda^3} = 40 \text{ min}$$

the electrons would accumulate energy and then would fly out all at once in large numbers, which contradicts the experimental facts.

2.15. $$N = \frac{n h c J}{e \lambda} = 930.$$

2.16. The energy of a photoelectron is determined by the energy needed to lift it over the potential barrier (work function) at the surface. This has in general a spread of values owing to the Pauli principle which leads to a range of energies for electrons in the conduction or valence bands of the solid (cf. problem 2.42).

2.17. (a) $1\cdot3 \times 10^8$ cm/sec (Cs); $7\cdot05 \times 10^7$ cm/sec (Pt).

(b) $6\cdot05 \times 10^7$ cm/sec (Cs);

no photoelectrons are knocked out from platinum.

2.18. $1\cdot73$ V.

2.19. $6\cdot55 \times 10^{-27}$ erg sec; $3\cdot74$ eV.

2.20.

$$p = \frac{h}{\lambda} + \sqrt{2m \left(\frac{h c}{\lambda} - A \right)} = 1\cdot31 \times 10^{-20} \text{ g} \cdot \text{cm/sec}.$$

Here A is the electron work function for the platinum surface.

2.21.

$$p = \sqrt{\left(\frac{h}{\lambda} \right)^2 + 2m \eta^2 \left(\frac{h c}{\lambda} - A \right)} = 3\cdot63 \times 10^{-22} \text{ g} \cdot \text{cm/sec}.$$

Here A is the work function for tungsten. The angle between the momentum direction of the particle and the direction of motion of the incident quantum is $48°$.

2.22. $\lambda = \dfrac{h\,c}{E_i + m_0\,c^2\left(\dfrac{n}{\sqrt{n^2 - 1}} - 1\right)} = 0{\cdot}043 \text{ Å},$

where m_0 is the rest mass of the electron.

2.23.

$$W_n = \frac{h\,c}{\lambda} + \frac{h^2}{2\,m}\left(\frac{3\,N\,\varrho}{8\pi\,\mu}\right)^{2/3} = 4{\cdot}19 \text{ eV}.$$

Here N is Avogadro's number, μ the atomic weight of potassium. The "red limit" of the photoeffect is determined by the electrons that fill the uppermost energy levels.

2.24. 2340 Å. The copper plate.

2.25. 5·29 eV.

2.27. (a) Those electrons may be treated as being free for which the binding energy is considerably smaller than that of the incoming photons.

(b) In this case the binding energy of the electrons is of the same order of magnitude as the energy of the incident quanta and consequently the free electron assumption of Compton may not be applied.

2.28. (a) This happens in both cases on account of the increase in the relative number of free electrons.

(b) Because the scattering occurs on free electrons.

(c) The undisplaced component is due to the scattering of photons on bound electrons.

2.29. 0·048 and 2·6 × 10⁻⁵ Å.

2.30. $\varDelta E = \dfrac{h\,c}{\lambda}\,\dfrac{2\varLambda \sin^2 \dfrac{\varphi}{2}}{\lambda + 2\varLambda \sin^2 \dfrac{\varphi}{2}},$ where $\varLambda = \dfrac{h}{m\,c}$

is the Compton wavelength; 120, 185 and 256 keV.

2.31. $\varphi = 50°$.

2.32.

(b) $\lambda = \dfrac{h\,c}{\varDelta E} - \dfrac{2h}{m\,c} = 0{\cdot}02 \text{ Å},$ $E_\varphi = 620 \text{ keV},$ $E_k = 439 \text{ keV}.$

2.33.
$$\lambda = \frac{\Delta \lambda}{2}\left(\sqrt{1 + \frac{4 h c}{E \Delta \lambda}} - 1\right),$$

where $\Delta \lambda$ is the Compton shift; E is the energy of the recoil electron.

(a)
$$E = \frac{1}{2 m_0}\left(\frac{e}{c}\varrho H\right)^2 \quad \text{and } \lambda = 0.43 \text{ Å}.$$

(b) In this case one can easily prove that the recoil electron is relativistic and that to find its energy one must use the relation $E^2 = p^2 c^2 + m_0^2 c^4$, which gives

$$E = \frac{m_0 c^2}{2}\left(\sqrt{1 + \left(\frac{e \varrho H}{m_0 c^2}\right)^2} - 1\right) \quad \text{and } \lambda = 0.0114 \text{ Å}.$$

2.34.
$$\tan \psi = \frac{\cot \dfrac{\varphi}{2}}{1 + \dfrac{h}{m c \lambda}}.$$

2.35. $109° \, 30'$.

2.36.
$$E = \frac{e U}{1 + \dfrac{2 e U}{m c^2}\sin^2\dfrac{\varphi}{2}} - E_i = 31 \text{ keV}.$$

2.37. (a) The broadening occurs firstly because the photons are scattered on moving electrons (the Doppler effect), and secondly because there is no sharp difference between free and bound electrons.

(b) According to the Doppler relation $\Delta \lambda/\lambda = v/c$; substituting $\Delta \lambda$ into this expression we obtain

$$v \approx \frac{h}{m \lambda}\sin^2\frac{\varphi}{2} \sim 10^8 \text{ cm/sec}.$$

2.38. (a) When a photon is completely absorbed by a free electron the laws of conservation of energy and momentum give:

$$h \nu = (m - m_0) c^2; \quad \frac{h}{\lambda} = m v.$$

Taking into account that $m = m_0/\sqrt{1 - \beta^2}$, where $\beta = v/c$, and

5 a*

combining the preceding relations we obtain $\beta = 0$ or 1. Neither of these results has any physical meaning.

(b) In a system of coordinates attached to the moving electron the energy of the latter is equal to $m_0 c^2$. In the same system the law of conservation of energy for emission of a photon is of the form

$$m_0 c^2 = m c^2 + h \nu.$$

It is evident at once that this cannot be true since $m > m_0$.

3.1. 5×10^{-12} cm.

3.2. $P = 3\cdot8 \times 10^{-12}$ cm; $r_0 = 4\cdot2 \times 10^{-12}$ cm.

3.3. The minimum distance $r_{\min}$ evidently occurs when $r = 0$ in the polar system of coordinates. From the laws of conservation of energy and momentum we have

$$\frac{m}{2}(\dot{r}^2 + r^2\,\dot{\vartheta}^2) + \frac{Z\,e^2}{r} = E,$$

$$m\,r^2\,\dot{\vartheta} = m\,v_0\,p,$$

where v_0 is the proton velocity at large distance from the atom, and p is the impact parameter. Eliminating $\dot{\vartheta}$, putting $\dot{r} = 0$ and expressing p as a function of the angle ϑ we find:

$$r_{\min} = \frac{Z\,e^2}{2\,E}\left(1 + \sqrt{1 + \cot^2\frac{\vartheta}{2}}\,\right) = 6\cdot28 \times 10^{-11}\ \text{cm}.$$

3.4. (a) In order to decrease the probability of double scattering.

(b) The observed correctness of Rutherford's formula proves firstly, that most of the mass of an atom (the nucleus) is indeed concentrated in a very small volume and, secondly, that the interaction between the incident charged particle and the nucleus is of Coulomb character up to very small distances between them ($\sim 10^{-12}$ cm). The departure from Rutherford's formula occurs for large values of the energy of the bombarding particles, when they penetrate into the range of nuclear forces. This occurs at lower energies in the case of scattering on light nuclei.

3.5. $r = \dfrac{Ze^2}{E} = 3 \times 10^{-12}$ cm.

3.6. For small angles of scattering we have large impact parameters and the nuclear charge is screened by the electrons.

3.8. 194 particles.

3.9.
$$q = \frac{2\,E\,L\sin^2\dfrac{\vartheta}{2}}{e}\sqrt{\frac{\eta\,A\,\sin\varphi}{\varrho\,\mathrm{d}S\,N}} = 47\,e,$$

where A is the atomic weight of silver, N Avogadro's number.

3.10.
$$d = \frac{4\,E^2\,\eta\,A\,\tan^2\dfrac{\vartheta_0}{2}}{\pi\,N\,\varrho\,Z^2\,e^4} = 0\cdot4\,\mu,$$

where A is the atomic weight of gold, Z its atomic number, N Avogadro's number, ϱ the density of gold.

3.12. (a)

$$\frac{1}{(\theta_2 - \theta_1)}\int_{\theta_1}^{\theta_2}\mathrm{d}\theta\,\frac{\mathrm{d}\theta}{\mathrm{d}\omega}\,\theta = \left(\frac{q_1\,q_2}{4\,E}\right)^2\int_{\theta_1}^{\theta_2}\frac{\mathrm{d}\theta}{\sin^4\theta/2}\cdot\frac{1}{(\theta_2 - \theta_1)}$$

$$= \left(\frac{q_1\,q_2}{4\,E}\right)^2\frac{1}{(\theta_2 - \theta_1)}\left[-\frac{\cot\theta}{3}\left(2 + \frac{1}{\sin^2\theta}\right)\right]_{\theta_1}^{\theta_2}$$

$$= 1\cdot3 \times 10^{-23}\,\mathrm{cm}^2$$

(b) 0·65 MeV.

3.13.
$$\varDelta\,\sigma = \frac{\eta\,A}{N\,\varrho\,d} = 15 \times 10^{-24}\,\mathrm{cm}^2,$$

where A is atomic weight of lead, N Avogadro's number.

3.14.
$$p = r_0^3\,E = 2 \times 10^{-24}\ \text{e.s.u.}$$

3.15.
$$\nu = \frac{1}{2\pi}\sqrt{\frac{e^2}{m\,r_0^3}} = 2\cdot5 \times 10^{15}\ \sec^{-1},$$

where e and m are the charge and the mass of the electron.

3.16. The Thomson model does not explain the experimental data on the scattering of alpha particles, nor the regularities in the spectra, also according to a theorem of electrostatics, it is completely unstable if maintained by electrostatic forces only.

3.17.
$$E\,(r_0) = \frac{2}{3}\frac{e^6}{m^2\,c^3\,r_0^4} = 0\cdot0364\ \text{erg/sec.}$$

For an orbit of half the radius, the radiative power is 16 times greater.

3.18. The emission of energy in a time dt occurs at the expense of the total energy W:

$$E(r)\, dt = -dW.$$

Substituting the corresponding expressions for $E(r)$ and W and integrating over r from r_0 to 0, we obtain:

$$\tau = \frac{m^2\, c^3\, r_0^3}{4\, e^4} \approx 10^{-10} \text{ sec.}$$

3.19. (b) $U_1 \approx 4{\cdot}9$ V. U_1 cannot be determined since, on account of the external contact potentials difference, the whole curve is displaced to the right.

(c) $\lambda \approx 0{\cdot}25\,\mu$.

	n	W_p, eV	W_k, eV	W_{tot}, eV
3.20. (a)	1	$-27{\cdot}2$	$13{\cdot}6$	$-13{\cdot}6$
	2	$-6{\cdot}8$	$3{\cdot}4$	$-3{\cdot}4$

(b) At all times (provided that the potential energy is taken to be zero at infinity).

(c) $2{\cdot}27 \times 10^{39}$.

3.21. By a factor 9.

3.22.
$$\nu = \frac{2\,|E|}{h\,n},$$

where n is the orbit number.

3.23.
$$\nu = \frac{4\pi^2\, m\, e^4}{h^3\, n^3} = \begin{cases} 6{\cdot}55 \times 10^{15} \text{ sec}^{-1}\ (n=1), \\ 0{\cdot}82 \times 10^{15} \text{ sec}^{-1}\ (n=2), \end{cases}$$
$$\nu_{12} = 2{\cdot}47 \times 10^{15} \text{ sec}^{-1}.$$

3.24. The correctness of the given equality can be easily shown by writing the revolution frequency of the electron in its nth orbit in the form

$$\nu = c\,R\,\frac{2}{n^3},$$

where R is Rydberg's constant and c the velocity of light. The rest can be seen without difficulty.

3.25. (a)
$$\mu_n = \frac{e\,h\,n}{4\pi\, m\, c} = \mu_0\, n,$$

where μ_0 is the Bohr magneton;

$$\frac{\mu_n}{p_n} = \frac{e}{2mc}.$$

(b) $\omega = 1.54 \times 10^{15}$ rad/sec; $E = -1.51$ eV.

3.26. $\Delta\mu = 2$ Bohr magnetons (cf. answer to 3.27).

3.27.

λ, Å	Series
1215	
1026	Lyman
973	
6570	
4860	Bahner
18750	Paschen

3.28. Three Lyman series lines.

3.29. $\Delta p = 2\hbar$.

3.30. $n = 4$.

3.31.

Transition $n_1 \to n_2$	U, v	λ, Å	$v \times 10^{-15}$, sec^{-1}	$\overline{v} \times 10^{-4}$, cm^{-1}
$2 \to 1$	10.2	1215	2.47	8.23
$\infty \to 1$	13.6	912	3.29	10.97

3.32. The Brackett series; $2.63\ \mu$.

3.34.
$$E_i = hc\,\frac{\lambda_1 + \lambda_2}{\lambda_1\,\lambda_2} = 13.6 \text{ eV}.$$

3.36.
$$n = 2\sqrt{\frac{R\,d\sin\varphi}{R\,d\sin\varphi - 4k}} = 4.$$

3.37. About 1900 lines.

3.38. 7×10^7 cm/sec relative to the nucleus.

3.39. The laws of conservation of energy and momentum (Fig. 38) give:

$$W_1 + \frac{M v_1^2}{2} = W_2 + \frac{M v_2^2}{2} + h\nu',$$

$$M(v_1 - v_2) = \frac{h\nu'}{c}\cos\vartheta.$$

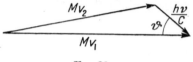

FIG. 38

Here W_1, W_2 and v_1 and v_2 represent respectively the intrinsic energies and the velocities of the atom before and after the emission of the photon, and M is the mass of the atom. The simultaneous solution of these equations, when the condition

$$W_1 - W_2 = h\nu$$

is taken into account, gives us the desired expression:

$$-\frac{\Delta\nu}{\nu} = \frac{\Delta\lambda}{\lambda} = \frac{v}{c}\cos\vartheta, \quad \text{where} \quad \Delta\nu = \nu - \nu'.$$

3.40. (a) $60\,500$ km/sec; (b) $\lambda = \dfrac{4\left(1 + \dfrac{v_r}{c}\right)}{3RZ^2} = 365\,\text{Å}$,

where v_r is the radial velocity of the galaxy, R Rydberg's constant and Z the atomic number of helium.

3.41. $\quad v = \dfrac{c}{\cos\vartheta}\left(\dfrac{3\lambda R}{4} - 1\right) \approx 7 \times 10^6$ cm/sec.

3.42. $\quad n_2 \to n_1$, where $n_1 = Z$, $n_2 = 2Z, 3Z, 4Z, \ldots$;

(Z is the charge number of the nucleus of the hydrogen-like ion).

3.43. $v_{\min} = 0.29c$ (c is the velocity of light). From the approximate Doppler expression

$$\nu' = \nu\left(1 + \frac{v}{c}\right)$$

we obtain $v \sim c$. This makes it necessary to use the exact expression for the Doppler shift

$$\nu' = \frac{\nu(1 + \beta)!}{\sqrt{1 - \beta^2}}, \quad \text{where} \quad \beta = v/c.$$

3.44. (a) Denote by R and r the distances from the nucleus and the electron respectively to the common centre of rotation. Then

$$\frac{M V^2}{R} = \frac{Z e^2}{a^2},$$

$$\frac{m v^2}{r} = \frac{Z e^2}{a^2},$$

here a is the distance between the particles, equal to $R + r$; M and m are the masses of the nucleus and the electron respectively and V and v are their velocities.

Using these expressions we can write

$$E_k = \frac{M V^2}{2} + \frac{m v^2}{2} = \frac{Z e^2}{2a}.$$

(b) The total energy is

$$E = E_k + E_p = -\frac{Z e^2}{2a}.$$

3.45. (a) Let us start from the following relations:

$$M \omega R^2 + m \omega r^2 = n \hbar \quad \text{(Bohr's condition)},$$

$$M \omega^2 R = \frac{Z e^2}{a^2},$$

$$m \omega^2 r = \frac{Z e^2}{a^2},$$

$$R + r = a,$$

where R and r denote the distances from the common centre of rotation to the nucleus and to the electron respectively; M and m are the masses of the two particles, ω their angular velocity.

From these expressions it follows that the distance between the electron and the nucleus is

$$a = \frac{\hbar^2 n^2}{Z \mu e^2},$$

where μ is the reduced mass, given by

$$\frac{m M}{m + M}.$$

Finally

$$\bar{\nu} = \frac{E_2 - E_1}{h c} = R Z^2 \left(\frac{1}{n_1^2} - \frac{1}{n_2^2} \right),$$

where

$$R = \frac{m\,e^4}{4\pi\,c\,h^3}\,\frac{1}{1 + \dfrac{m}{M}} = \frac{R_\infty}{1 + \dfrac{m}{M}}\,.$$

(b)

$$\mu_p = \frac{e\,\omega}{2\,c}\,(R^2 - r^2) = \frac{e\,\hbar\,n}{2c}\left(\frac{1}{m} - \frac{1}{M}\right).$$

3.46.

	$\Delta\,\lambda$, Å	$\Delta\,U_1$, mV	$\Delta\,U_i$, mV
(a)	0·33	2·78	3·7
(b)	0·11	0·92	1·23

3.47. (a) Yes.

(b) No (cf. answer to 3.45 for details).

3.48.

$$m = \frac{M_n(1 - \eta)}{\eta - \dfrac{M_{\mathrm H}}{M_{\mathrm{He}}}} = 9{\cdot}1 \times 10^{-28}\ \mathrm{g}.$$

3.49.

$$a_1 = \frac{\hbar^2\,n^2}{\mu\,e^2} = 1{\cdot}05\ \text{Å}\quad (n = 1),$$

$$U_i = \frac{R\,h\,c}{e} = \frac{m\,e^3}{4\hbar^2} = 6{\cdot}8\mathrm{V}\quad \mu = 0.$$

3.50. $2{\cdot}81 \times 10^{-11}$ cm; $6{\cdot}45$ Å.

3.51. $2{\cdot}07 \times 10^7$ cm^{-1}; $1{\cdot}92$ and $2{\cdot}56$ kV.

4.1. (a) $\quad \Psi(x, t) = A\, e^{2\pi i (kx - \nu t)} = A\, e^{\frac{i}{h}(px - Et)}$,

(b) $\quad \Psi(r, t) = A\, e^{2\pi i (kx - \nu t)} = A\, e^{\frac{i}{h}(pr - Et)}$.

4.2. 12·3; 0·287 and 0·0186 Å.

4.3. 4 × 10^{-4} Å.

4.4. 7270 and 3·96 km/sec, 150 and 0·082 eV.

4.5. $\qquad\qquad \lambda = \dfrac{h\,c}{e\,\varrho\,H} = 1\text{·}8 \text{ Å.}$

4.6. 4·78 × 10^8 cm/sec.

4.7. $\qquad\qquad T = \dfrac{\pi\, h^2\, n_0^{2/3}}{8\, m\, k\, \eta^2} = 33\text{·}5°\text{K.}$

Here n_0 is Avogadro's number, m the mass of the molecule and k Boltzmann's constant.

4.8. $\qquad\qquad \Delta n = a\, e^{-h^2/2mkT\lambda^2} \dfrac{\Delta \lambda}{\lambda^4},$

where a is a certain constant, m the mass of the particle and k Boltzmann's constant.

4.9. From the condition $\mathrm{d}f/\mathrm{d}\lambda = 0$, where f is the distribution function of the particles over de Broglie wavelengths, we find

$$\lambda_w = \frac{h}{2\sqrt{m\,k\,T}} = 0\text{·}9 \text{ A.}$$

4.10. $\qquad\qquad \dfrac{\mathrm{d}\lambda}{\mathrm{d}t} = - \dfrac{h\,e\,E}{2\,m\,E} = -59\text{·}4\,\mu/\text{sec.}$

4.11. (a) $\lambda' - \lambda = \dfrac{h}{m\,v}\dfrac{k}{1 - k}$, $\quad v' - v = \dfrac{m\,v^2}{2\,h}\, k\,(k - 2)$

for $k = 2$ the apparent electron velocity is just the negative of the original velocity.

(b) $\qquad\qquad \Delta \lambda = 2\text{·}33 \text{ Å}, \quad \Delta \nu = -4\text{·}64 \times 10^{15} \text{ sec}^{-1}.$

4.12. $\qquad E = \dfrac{h^2}{2\,m\,d^2} \approx (1\cdot3 - 0\cdot2)\,10^{-2}\,\text{eV}.$

4.13. $\qquad \lambda = \dfrac{h}{\sqrt{2\,m_0\,e\,U}}\;\dfrac{1}{\sqrt{1 + \dfrac{e\,U}{2\,m_0\,c^2}}},$

where U is the accelerating potential; m_0 is the rest mass of the particle.

4.14. From the answer to the preceding problem it follows that when $\qquad e\,U \ll m_0\,c^2$ we have

$$\lambda \approx \lambda_0\left(1 - \frac{e\,U}{4\,m_0\,c^2}\right), \quad \text{where} \quad \lambda_0 = \frac{h}{\sqrt{2\,m_0\,e\,U}},$$

whence

$$E_k = e\,U \approx 4\,m_0\,c^2\,\frac{\Delta\lambda}{\lambda_0}.$$

(a) $\qquad\qquad\qquad$ 20·4 keV,
(b) $\qquad\qquad\qquad$ 37·5 MeV,
(c) $\qquad\qquad\qquad$ 75 MeV.

4.15. $\qquad E_k = m_0\,c^2\,(\sqrt{2} - 1) = 0\cdot21\,\text{MeV}.$

In carrying out the calculation it should be taken into account that such an electron is relativistic.

4.16. $\qquad \lambda = \dfrac{h\,c}{E} = 2\cdot07 \times 10^{-14}\,\text{cm}.$

To "explore" the structure of nuclei and of elementary particles, whose dimensions are of the order of 10^{-12} cm or less, it is necessary to use particles of wavelength considerably smaller than the nuclei themselves.

4.17. $\qquad \lambda = \dfrac{h^2\,n}{2\pi\,m\,Z\,e^2}\,; \quad 3\cdot32 \text{ and } 6\cdot64\,\text{Å}.$

4.18. From the laws of conservation of energy and momentum we have

$$\lambda = h\sqrt{\frac{m + M}{2\,m\,(M - m)\,E}} = 1\cdot17 \times 10^{-2}\,\text{Å},$$

where m is the mass of the proton and M the mass of the scattering nucleus.

4.19. $$d = \frac{k\,h}{2\,\cos\dfrac{a}{2}\,\sqrt{2m\,E}} = 2.06 \text{ Å}.$$

At an angle of $27.5°$.

4.20. $$d \approx \frac{2\,k\,h\,L}{D\,\sqrt{2m\,e\,U}} = 4.03 \text{ Å},$$

where k is the order of reflection.

4.21. (a) $$\sin\vartheta = \frac{k\,h}{2d\,\sqrt{2m_0 E\left(1 + \dfrac{E}{2m_0 c^2}\right)}}.$$

From here $$2\vartheta = 3°23'.$$

(b) For example, by means of a magnet.

4.22. $$n = \sqrt{\frac{E_0 + e\,U_i}{E_0}}.$$

4.23. 12 V.

4.24. $$n = 1.048; \quad \vartheta' = \arcsin\left(\frac{\cos\vartheta}{n}\right) = 42.5°;$$

$$v' = \sqrt{\frac{2(E + e\,U_i)}{m}} = 6.81 \times 10^8 \text{ cm/sec}.$$

4.25. As shown in Fig. 39 the optical path difference of rays 1 and 2 is

$$A\,B\,C - D\,C = \frac{2d}{\sin\vartheta'}\,n - 2d\,\cot\vartheta'\,\cos\vartheta.$$

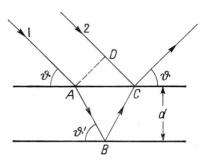

FIG. 39

The intensity maximum of a ray specularly reflected from this system of planes will occur when the path difference is equal to a whole number of wavelengths. Hence one can easily obtain the final expression:

$$2d\sqrt{n^2 - \cos^2 \vartheta} = k\lambda.$$

4.26. $2\cdot7$ Å.

4.27. $\qquad d \approx 0\cdot2$ Å; $\lambda = 3\cdot69 \times 10^{-2}$ Å

(when the relativistic correction is taken into account).

4.28. $\qquad E = m_0 c^2 \left[\sqrt{1 + \left(\frac{1\cdot22\, h\, A}{m_0\, c\, D}\right)^2} - 1 \right] \approx 83\,\text{keV}$

where m_0 is the rest mass of the electron and c the velocity of light.

4.29. $\qquad g = \dfrac{d\nu}{dk} = \dfrac{dE}{dp} = \dfrac{p}{m} = v \quad (v \ll c),$

$$g = \frac{d}{dp}\sqrt{p^2 c^2 + m_0^2 c^4} = v \quad (v \sim c).$$

4.30. $\Delta v/v \approx 6 \times 10^{-7}$.

4.31. $\Delta v \sim 5\cdot3 \times 10^{-21}$ cm/sec whence it is evident, that in this case the uncertainty relation has no practical meaning.

4.32. $\qquad \Delta v \sim 10^8$ cm/sec; $v = 2{,}18 \times 10^8$ cm/sec.

4.33. Dividing and multiplying the left-hand side of the relation

$$\Delta x\, \Delta p_x \geqq \hbar$$

by the radius of the orbit of the electron, we have

$$\Delta \varphi\, \Delta L \geqq \hbar,$$

where φ is the angular coordinate of the electron, and L its angular momentum.

Hence it is evident that the angle φ is completely indeterminate

$$(\Delta \varphi \geqq 2\pi) \quad \text{for } \frac{\Delta L}{L} \leqq 16\%.$$

4.34. $0\cdot6 \times 10^{-8}$ and $0\cdot5 \times 10^{-12}$ cm.

4.35. (a) ~3 m; (b) $1\cdot6 \times 10^{-4}$ Å.

4.36. In this case the ratio of the electron momentum component perpendicular to the trajectory to the momentum itself is a negligibly small quantity:

$$\frac{\Delta \, p_x}{p_x} \sim 6 \times 10^{-7}.$$

Consequently (when $\Delta p_x < p_x$) the concept of trajectory has a definite physical meaning: the trajectories are strictly rectilinear and do not show any departure from the laws of classical mechanics.

4.37.
$$d = \sqrt[4]{\frac{2\,\hbar^2\,l^2}{m\,E}} \approx 6 \, \mu;$$

for electrons $d \approx 40 \, \mu$.

4.38. (a)
$$E \sim \frac{\hbar^2}{8\,m\,l^2} \sim 4 \; \text{eV}.$$

(b) Direct calculation shows that in this case the electron is relativistic, and hence

$$E = \sqrt{p^2\,c^2 + m_0^2\,c^4} - m_0\,c^2,$$

where m_0 is the rest mass of the electron. Taking into account the relation $p \sim \hbar/l$, we find that $E \approx 19 \cdot 2$ MeV.

4.39. The energy of the electron

$$E = \frac{p^2}{2\,m} + e\,E\,x,$$

when the relation $x \sim \hbar/p$ is taken into account, is

$$E \sim \frac{p^2}{2\,m} + \frac{\hbar\,e\,E}{p}.$$

The minimum of E occurs when $\mathrm{d}E/\mathrm{d}p = 0$, whence

$$p \sim \sqrt[3]{\hbar\,m\,e\,E} = 3 \cdot 58 \times 10^{-20} \; \text{g cm/sec}.$$

At the same time, this is the uncertainty in the momentum of the electron.

4.40. When the relation $p \sim \hbar/2\,|x|$ is taken into account, the energy of the particle is

$$E = \frac{p^2}{2\,m} + k\,|\,x\,|^3 \sim \frac{\hbar^2 + 8\,m\,k\,|\,x\,|^5}{8\,m\,|\,x\,|^2}.$$

From the condition $\mathrm{d}E/\mathrm{d}x = 0$ we find that

$$\varDelta x \sim 2\,|x| = \sqrt[5]{\frac{8\,\hbar^2}{3\,m\,k}}\,.$$

4.41. The expression for the energy of an oscillator is

$$E = \frac{p^2}{2\,\mu} + \frac{k\,x^2}{2} \sim \frac{\hbar^2 + 4\,\mu\,k\,x^4}{8\,\mu\,x^2}\,,$$

where p is the momentum, μ the reduced mass and k the elastic force modulus. On the right hand side it was taken into account that $p \sim \hbar/2x$. From the condition that $\mathrm{d}E/\mathrm{d}x = 0$ we easily find the required value for $E_{\min}$:

$$E_{\min} \sim \frac{\hbar}{2}\sqrt{\frac{k}{\mu}} = \frac{h\,\nu}{2}\,.$$

4.42. The energy of such an electron is

$$E = \frac{p^2}{2\,m} - \frac{Z\,e^2}{r} \sim \frac{\hbar^2}{2\,m\,r^2} - \frac{Z\,e^2}{r}\,,$$

where the uncertainty relation $p \sim \hbar/r$ has been taken into account and it has also been assumed that the other electrons do not screen the field of the nucleus for the electron in question. Hence one can easily find the value of r that makes E a minimum and also the value of $E_{\min}$ itself:

$$E_{\min} \sim -\frac{m\,Z^2\,e^4}{2\,\hbar^2}\,.$$

For the hydrogen atom $E_{\min} \sim -13{\cdot}6$ eV, which is exactly equal to the well-known value.

4.43. The energy of the two electrons of a helium atom in the field of the nucleus is

$$E \sim 2\left(\frac{p^2}{2\,m} - \frac{Z\,e^2}{r}\right) + \frac{e^2}{2\,r}\,,$$

where p is the momentum of each electron and the last term describes the interaction energy between the electrons. Putting $p \sim \hbar/r$ we find

$$E \sim \frac{2\,\hbar^2 + m\,r\,e^2(1 - 4Z)}{2\,m\,r^2}\,.$$

Hence we easily obtain the minimum value of E:

$$E_{\min} \sim -\frac{m\, e^4 (4Z - 1)^2}{16\, h^2} = -83.5 \text{ eV},$$

which is in good agreement with the experimental data.

4.44. If a_0 is the wave amplitude (whose square is well known to be proportional to the density of the particle flux), then an elementary de Broglie wave

$$\mathrm{d}\Psi = a_0\, \mathrm{d}x\, \mathrm{e}^{i(\omega t - kx \sin \varphi)},$$

propagates in the direction φ, where $k = 2\pi/\lambda$, through an element $\mathrm{d}x$ at distance x from the top of the slit (Fig. 40).

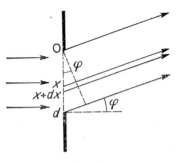

FIG. 40

Taking into account the interference in the direction φ from all elements of the slit, we obtain

$$\Psi = \int_0^d \mathrm{d}\Psi = \frac{i\, a_0}{k \sin \varphi} \left(1 - \mathrm{e}^{-ikd \sin \varphi}\right).$$

The following expression defines the distribution of the particles:

$$W = \Psi\, \Psi^* = \frac{a_0^2 \sin^2 \left(\dfrac{k\, d \sin \varphi}{2}\right)}{\left(\dfrac{k \sin \varphi}{2}\right)^2}.$$

Evidently, $W = 0$ for $\dfrac{k\, d \sin \varphi}{2} = \pm\, n\, \pi$, where $n = 1, 2, 3, \ldots$

Hence and from geometrical considerations we find the distance from the center of the diffraction pattern to the first minimum to be

$$r \approx \frac{hL}{d\sqrt{2mE}},$$

where h is Planck's constant.

4.45. Using the condition that the waves be extinguished in the direction φ, we have

$$d \sin \varphi = \lambda/2,$$

where d is the slit width and λ the de Broglie wavelength.

The uncertainty in the value of the momentum is

$$\Delta p \gtrsim p \sin \varphi = \frac{h}{\lambda} \sin \varphi.$$

Comparing the two expressions we get:

$$d \Delta p \gtrsim h.$$

4.46. Taking into account that a wave packet represents a superposition of de Broglie waves, we write

$$\Psi(x, t) = \int_{k_0 - \Delta k}^{k_0 + \Delta k} A(k) \, e^{i(kx - \omega t)} \, dk,$$

where $k = 2\pi/\lambda$. For simplicity we shall consider the wave packet at the time $t = 0$, which will not affect the generality of the final result. We shall also assume that the amplitude $A(k)$ is a slowly varying function of the wave number k. Then

$$\Psi(x, 0) = A(k_0) \, e^{ik_0 x} \int_{-\Delta k}^{\Delta k} e^{i\Delta k x} \, dk.$$

Integrating, we obtain

$$\Psi(x, 0) = A(k_0) \, e^{ik_0 x} \, 2\Delta k \, \frac{\sin(\Delta k \, x)}{\Delta k \, x}.$$

Hence the probability density for finding the particle at x is

$$W(x, 0) = \Psi \Psi^* \sim \frac{\sin^2(\Delta k \, x)}{(\Delta k \, x)^2}.$$

The form of this function is represented in Fig. 41. This shows that the probability differs from zero practically only in the region enclosed between the first minima of the function, that is, in the interval $(-\pi, +\pi)$. The total width of the region is

$$\Delta \zeta = \Delta k \Delta x \gtrsim 2\pi.$$

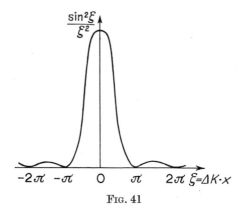

FIG. 41

Passing from Δk to Δp (the uncertainty in defining the value of the momentum) we finally have

$$\Delta p \Delta x \gtrsim h.$$

5.1.
$$\Psi(x, t) = A\, e^{i\frac{m}{\hbar}\left(vx - \frac{v^2}{2}t\right)}.$$

5.2.
$$\Psi(r, t) = A\, e^{i\frac{m}{\hbar}\left(vr - \frac{v^2}{2}t\right)}.$$

5.3. The wave function that describes the motion of a particle in a moving coordinates system K' is of the form:

$$\Psi'(x', t) = A\, e^{2\pi i (k' x' - \nu' t)}.$$

Let us transform the exponent by means of the following relations:

$$x' = x - v_0\, t,$$

$$k' = \frac{m(v - v_0)}{h} = k\left(1 - \frac{v_0}{v}\right),$$

$$v' = \frac{m(v - v_0)^2}{2h} = v - \frac{m\, v_0}{2h}(2v - v_0).$$

We finally have:

$$\Psi'(x', t) = \Psi(x, t)\, e^{-\frac{i}{\hbar}\left(mv_0 x - \frac{m v_0^2}{2}t\right)}.$$

It is evident that the exponential term describes the motion of a particle together with the system K', relative to the system K.

5.4. (a)
$$\nabla^2\psi + \frac{2m}{\hbar^2}\left(E - \frac{k\, r^2}{2}\right)\psi = 0.$$

(b)
$$\nabla^2\psi + \frac{2m}{\hbar^2}\left(E - \frac{q_1 q_2}{r}\right)\psi = 0.$$

Here ∇^2 is the Laplace operator in a spherical polar coordinate system, m the mass of the particle, q_1 and q_2 the charges of the particle and of the Coulomb force centre.

5.5. In a cartesian system we have

$$\frac{\partial^2\psi}{\partial x^2} + \frac{\partial^2\psi}{\partial y^2} + \frac{2m}{\hbar^2}(E - U)\psi = 0.$$

To transform to polar coordinates we use the relations

$$x = r \cos \varphi, \quad y = r \sin \varphi,$$

or

$$r^2 = x^2 + y^2, \quad \tan \varphi = \frac{y}{x},$$

and also the expressions for the transformation of derivatives

$$\frac{\partial}{\partial x} = \frac{\partial \varphi}{\partial x} \frac{\partial}{\partial \varphi} + \frac{\partial r}{\partial x} \frac{\partial}{\partial r}$$

and similarly for $\partial/\partial y$.

After carrying out these transformations we have:

$$\frac{1}{r} \frac{\partial}{\partial r} \left(r \frac{\partial \psi}{\partial r} \right) + \frac{1}{r^2} \frac{\partial^2 \psi}{\partial \varphi^2} + \frac{2m}{\hbar^2} (E - U) \psi = C.$$

5.6. If U does not depend explicity on time, it can be easily seen that the Schrödinger equation

$$i \hbar \frac{\partial \Psi}{\partial t} = \frac{\hbar}{2m} \Delta \Psi - U \Psi,$$

may be solved by the method of separation of variables:

$$\Psi (x, t) = \psi (x) \varphi (t).$$

Substituting this solution into the equation, we finally have

$$\Psi_n (x, t) = \psi_n (x)\, e^{-i \frac{E_n}{\hbar} t},$$

where the $\psi_n(x)$ are the eigenfunctions and the E_n are the eigenvalues of the energy parameter.

Evidently, the wave function depends harmonically on time and hence the probability of finding the particle at a given position, i.e. $|\psi|^2$ or $\psi\psi^*$ (where ψ^* is the complex conjugate function) is not time-dependent. Such states are therefore called stationary.

5.7. One can easily see that the change of sign in the Schrödinger equation only changes the sign of the time in the exponential part of the wave function. Thus, for example, in place of

$$\Psi (x, t) = \psi_n (x)\, e^{-i \frac{E_n}{\hbar} t}$$

we have

$$\Psi (x, t) = \psi_n (x)\, e^{i \frac{E_n}{\hbar} t}.$$

As was shown in the preceding problem, such a dependence of the wave function on time occurs when the function U is not explicitly time-dependent. Since only the probabilities, i.e. $|\psi|^2$, have physical meaning, and since they are evidently the same for both signs, it follows that the sign in the Schrödinger equation indeed has no meaning in this case.

5.8. For a Schrödinger equation extending over a finite region of space, the discreteness of the energy eigenvalues follows by imposition of boundary conditions. The existence of such boundary conditions may be taken as a postulate of wave-mechanics. For a system extending over the whole of space, discrete eigenvalues result, provided there is a suitable attractive potential, from the requirements of continuity and boundedness of the wave function and its derivatives.

5.9. Putting $U(x) = 0$ in the Schrödinger equation, we find its solution to be:

$$\psi(x) = a\, e^{\pm i \frac{\sqrt{2mE}}{\hbar} x}.$$

As can be easily seen, this solution satisfies the standard conditions for all values of $E > 0$.

5.10. Since the walls of the potential well are absolutely opaque for a particle, the probability of its occupying a given position differs from zero only within the region $0 < x < l$. Consequently, outside this region the wave function of the particle must be identically zero.

In this region the Schrödinger equation is

$$\psi'' + k^2 \psi = 0, \quad \text{where} \quad k = \sqrt{2mE}/\hbar.$$

Its general solution is

$$\psi(x) = a_1 \sin k\,x + a_2 \cos k\,x,$$

where a_1 and a_2 are arbitrary constants to be defined.† From the boundary conditions $\psi(0) = 0$ and $\psi(l) = 0$ we have $\sin kl = 0$ from where $kl = \pm n\pi, n = 1, 2, 3, ...$; the value $n = 0$ corresponds to $\psi(x) = 0$, that is, there is no particle.

---

† The general solution of this equation can equally well be chosen in another form, for example $\psi = a \sin(k\,x + \alpha)$ or $\psi = a_1 e^{i k x} + a_2 e^{-i k x}$.

Solving for k we find

$$E_n = \frac{\pi^2 \, h^2 \, n^2}{2 \, m \, l^2}.$$

To obtain the final form of the corresponding wave functions we must find the value of the constant a_1. From the normalization condition it follows that

$$\int_0^l a_1^2 \sin^2 k \, x \, \mathrm{d}x = 1.$$

This means that the total probability of finding the particle in the well is 1, as the problem requires (a certainty). Hence

$$a_1 = \sqrt{\frac{2}{l}}$$

and

$$\Psi_n(x, t) = \sqrt{\frac{2}{l}} \sin \frac{\pi \, x \, n}{l} \, \mathrm{e}^{\pm i \frac{E_n}{\hbar} t}.$$

5.11. *Hint:* The property of orthogonality of the eigenfunctions ψ_n and ψ_m requires that

$$\int_{-\infty}^{+\infty} \psi_n \, \psi_m \, \mathrm{d}x = 0$$

for $n \neq m$.

5.13. $\bar{x} = \int_{-\infty}^{+\infty} x \, \psi_n^2(x) \, \mathrm{d}x$. Here the $\psi_n(x)$ must be taken to be the normalized eigenfunctions of the particle. The fact that $\psi_n(x) = 0$ outside the interval $(0, l)$, permits us in this case to confine the integration to the range from 0 to l.

5.14. (a) The Schrödinger equation in this case is of the form:

$$\frac{1}{r_0^2} \frac{\mathrm{d}^2 \psi}{\mathrm{d}\varphi^2} + \frac{2 \, m}{\hbar^2} E \, \psi = 0.$$

We write the solution of this equation in the form

$$\psi = a \, \mathrm{e}^{ik\varphi},$$

where $k = r_0 \sqrt{2 \, m \, E} / \hbar$. In order that the wave function be single valued is required, we must have that

$$\psi(\varphi) = \psi(\varphi + 2\pi),$$

whence

$$k = \pm n, \quad n = 1, 2, 3, \ldots$$

($n = 0$ corresponds to the case when there is no particle).
Solving for k, we finally have

$$E_n = \frac{h^2 n^2}{2 m r_0^2}.$$

The possible values of the angular momentum of the particle are easily found to be $p_n = n h$.

Note that the expression obtained for E_n follows directly from the requirement that a whole number of de Broglie waves should fit into the given circumference length

$$n \lambda = 2 \pi r_0.$$

(a) From the normalization condition of the wave function it follows that

$$\int\limits_0^{2\pi} a^2 \sin^2 (k \varphi + \alpha) \, d\varphi = 1,$$

whence

$$a = \frac{1}{\sqrt{\pi}} \text{ and } \psi_n = \frac{1}{\sqrt{\pi}} \sin (n \varphi + \alpha), \text{ where } n = 1, 2, 3, \ldots$$

5.15. (a) Let us write down the Schrödinger equation for the region inside the potential well:

$$\frac{\partial^2 \psi}{\partial x^2} + \frac{\partial^2 \psi}{\partial y^2} + \frac{2m}{h^2} E \psi = 0.$$

Since the wave function has nodes (becomes zero) at the boundaries of the well, where $x = 0$ and $y = 0$, one immediately seeks a solution in the form of a product of sines:

$$\psi = a \sin k_1 x \sin k_2 y.$$

We find the values of k_1 and k_2 at once from the condition that $\psi = 0$ for $x = l_1$, and $y = l_2$. Hence

$$k_1 = \pm \frac{\pi}{l_1} n_1, \quad n_1 = 1, 2, 3, \ldots$$

$$k_2 = \pm \frac{\pi}{l_2} n_2, \quad n_2 = 1, 2, 3, \ldots$$

Substituting the wave function ψ into the Schrödinger equation we obtain an expression that gives the allowed values of the energy of the particle:

$$E = \frac{\pi^2 \hbar^2}{2m}\left(\frac{n_1^2}{l_1^2} + \frac{n_2^2}{l_2^2}\right).$$

It may be observed that the lowest value of the energy of the particle cannot be equal to zero. For $l_1 = l_2$ the energy levels become degenerate.

$$\psi_{n_1 n_2}(x, y) = \frac{2}{\sqrt{l_1 l_2}} \sin\frac{\pi n_1 x}{l_1} \sin\frac{\pi n_2 y}{l_2}.$$

5.16. Let us integrate the Schrödinger equation

$$\psi_x'' + \frac{2m}{\hbar^2}(E - U)\,\psi = 0$$

over a narrow region in which the discontinuity of potential is included (the neighbourhood of the point $x = 0$):

$$\psi_\delta' - \psi_{-\delta}' = \int_{-\delta}^{\delta} \frac{2m}{\hbar^2}(U - E)\,\psi\,\mathrm{d}x.$$

The change in U is finite within the range of integration, so that for $\delta \to 0$ the integral also tends to zero. Hence

$$\psi_0' = \psi_{-0}'.$$

5.17. Let us write down the Schrödinger equation for the two regions:

$(0 \leq x \leq l)\ \psi_1'' + k_1^2\,\psi_1 = 0,$ where $k_1 = \sqrt{2mE}/\hbar,$

$(l \leq x)\ \psi_2'' + k_2^2\,\psi_2 = 0,$ where $k_2 = \sqrt{2m(E - U_0)}/\hbar.$

The general solutions

$$\psi_1 = a_1 \sin k_1 x + a_2 \cos k_1 x,$$
$$\psi_2 = b_1 \sin k_2 x + b_2 \cos k_2 x$$

should satisfy the following boundary conditions:

$$\psi_1(0) = 0,$$
$$\psi_1(l) = \psi_2(l),$$
$$\psi_1'(l) = \psi_2'(l),$$

or, explicitly

$$a_1 \sin k_1 l = b_1 \sin k_2 l + b_2 \cos k_2 l,$$

$$k_1 a_1 \cos k_1 l = k_2 (b_1 \cos k_2 l - b_2 \sin k_2 l).$$

From these expressions one can eliminate only two of the three constants $(a_1, b_1$ and $b_2)$, for example b_1 and b_2, so that we have

$$f(k_1, k_2, a_1) = 0,$$

which is satisfied for any value of the energy E within the range $E > U_0$.

5.18. (a) We write down the Schrödinger equations for the two regions:

$$(0 \leqq x \leqq l)\ \psi_1'' + k_1^2 \psi_1 = 0, \quad \text{where} \quad k_1 = \sqrt{2m\,E}/\hbar,$$

$$(l \leqq x)\ \psi_2'' - k_2^2 \psi_2 = 0, \quad \text{where} \quad k_2 = \sqrt{2m(U_0 - E)}/\hbar.$$

The general solutions

$$\psi_1 = a_1 \sin k_1 x + a_2 \cos k_1 x,$$

$$\psi_2 = b_1 e^{k_2 x} + b_2 e^{-k_2 x}$$

must satisfy the boundary conditions and the normalization conditions for the wave functions. In order that the wave function should nowhere become infinite it is necessary that $b_1 = 0$. Also, from the condition $\psi_1 = 0$ it is evident that $a_2 = 0$. From the boundary conditions at the point $x = l$ we get

$$a_1 \sin k_1 l = b_2 e^{-k_2 l},$$

$$k_1 a_1 \cos k_1 l = -k_2 b_2 e^{-k_2 l}.$$

We eliminate a_1 and b_2, and so obtain

$$k_2 \tan k_1 l = -k_1$$

or

$$\tan \frac{l \sqrt{2m\,E}}{\hbar} = -\sqrt{\frac{E}{U_0 - E}}.$$

(b) Representing graphically the left and right hand sides of this expression (Fig. 42), we find points of intersection which correspond to the negative values of the tangent. The abscissae of these points represent the allowed values of energy (more precisely of $\sqrt{E}$), which together form the discrete energy spectrum $(1, 2, 3, \ldots)$.

(c) It is evident from Fig. 42 that in a well of finite depth $(U_0$ finite) there can be a finite number of allowed energy values.

6*

The dotted curve gives the limiting case: it defines the conditions for which there are no intersections. The conditions for this are

$$U_0 \leqq E,$$

where E is defined from the condition that the tangent becomes infinite:

$$\frac{l\sqrt{2mE}}{\hbar} = \frac{\pi}{2}.$$

Hence

$$U_0 \leqq \frac{\pi^2 \hbar^2}{8ml^2}.$$

For such a potential well there are no allowed energy levels.

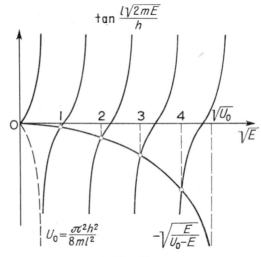

FIG. 42

5.19. (a) There is a finite probability of finding the particle in the region where $x > 0$, i.e., even where $E < U_0$. This apparently paradoxical result, not allowed within the framework of classical mechanics, is due purely to the quantum effect. It results from the fact that the particle has wave properties which do not allow the simultaneous exact determination of the coordinates and the momentum. Consequently, it does not allow an exact simultaneous separation of total energy into potential and kinetic energy. This can be done only within the limits of accuracy allowed by the uncertainty relation.

(b) Within the limits of the well

$$W = \psi_1^2 = c_1 \sin^2 k_1 x, \quad \text{where} \quad k_1 = \sqrt{2m\,E}/\hbar\,;$$

outside the well

$$W = c_2\,e^{-2k_2 x}, \quad \text{where} \quad k_2 = \sqrt{2m\,(U_0 - E)}/\hbar$$

(c_1 and c_2 are some constants)

(c)
$$\frac{W_{l\infty}}{W_{0l}} = \frac{\int\limits_{l}^{\infty} \psi_2^2\,\mathrm{d}x}{\int\limits_{0}^{l} \psi_1^2\,\mathrm{d}x} = \frac{2\,k_1 \sin^2 k_1 l}{k_2\,(2\,k_1\,l - \sin 2\,k_1\,l)}\,.$$

5.20. The ψ function should be of the form shown in Fig. 43. This can be easily understood from the following arguments: on the left the particle moves faster (its kinetic energy is greater), and hence the wavelength of the ψ-function should be smaller.

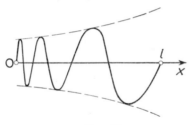

FIG. 43

At the same time, the probability of finding the particle, and consequently the amplitude of the ψ function, should also be smaller here. Finally, on account of the impenetrability of the walls of the potential well, the ψ-function should have nodes at the points $x = 0$ and $x = l$.

5.21. (a) Let us write down the Schrödinger equation and its general solutions for the three regions ($x \leqq 0$, $0 \leqq x \leqq l$, $x \geqq l$). From the boundary conditions and the quantum mechanical postulates we have the required expression

$$\tan k_0\,l = -\frac{2\,k_0\,k}{k^2 - k_0^2}\,,$$

where $\qquad k_0 = \sqrt{2m\,E}/\hbar, \ \ k = \sqrt{2m(U_0 - E)}/\hbar;$

or finally $\qquad \tan \dfrac{l\,\sqrt{2m\,E}}{\hbar} = -\dfrac{2\,\sqrt{E(U_0 - E)}}{U_0 - 2E}.$

(b) Let us represent graphically the left and the right-hand sides of the last expression as function of $\sqrt{E}$ (Fig. 44). The abscissae of the points of intersection define the discrete energy spectrum of the particle. Contrary to the case of the potential well in Fig. 8,

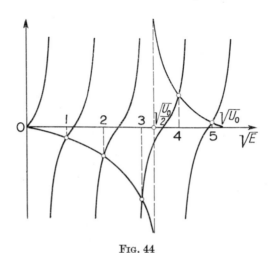

Fig. 44

it can be easily seen in this case that intersection points (solutions) exist, always i.e., for any depth or width of the potential well. Compare this with the solution of problem 5.18.

5.23. First we find the wave functions that describe the motion of the particle outside and inside the potential well:

$$(0 \leqq 0) \quad \psi_1 = a\,e^{kx},$$

$$(0 \leqq x \leqq l) \quad \psi_2 = b_1 \sin k_0\,x + b_2 \cos k_0\,x,$$

$$(x \geqq l) \quad \psi_3 = c\,e^{-kx},$$

where

$$k = \sqrt{2m(U_0 - E)}/\hbar, \ \ k_0 = \sqrt{2m\,E}/\hbar.$$

From the boundary conditions it follows that

$$a = b_2,$$
$$a\,k = b_1\,k_0.$$

Setting the probabilities equal, we have

$$2 \int_{-\infty}^{0} a^2\,e^{2kx}\,\mathrm{d}x = \int_{0}^{l} (b_1 \sin k_0\,x + b_2 \cos k_0\,x)^2\,\mathrm{d}x.$$

Integrating and expressing b_1 and b_2 in terms of a, we obtain the required condition:

$$(k^2 - k_0^2) \sin 2k_0\,l = 4k_0\,k \sin^2 k_0\,l + 4k_0^3 \left(l - \frac{1}{k}\right).$$

5.24. (a) $$\tan [k_2(l_2 - l_1)] = \frac{k_2(k_3 \tan k_1\,l_1 + k_1)}{k_2^2 \tan k_1\,l_1 - k_1\,k_3},$$

where

$$k_1 = \sqrt{2m\,E}/\hbar, \quad k_2 = \sqrt{2m(E - U_1)}/\hbar, \quad k_3 = \sqrt{2m(U_2 - E)}/\hbar.$$

(b) $$e^{2k_2(l_2 - l_1)} = \frac{(k_2 - k_3)\,(k_2 \tan k_1\,l_1 - k_1)}{(k_2 + k_3)\,(k_2 \tan k_1\,l_1 + k_1)},$$

where

$$k_1 = \sqrt{2m\,E}/\hbar, \quad k_2 = \sqrt{2m(U_1 - E)}/\hbar, \quad k_3 = \sqrt{2m(U_2 - E)}/\hbar.$$

5.25. This problem can best be solved in polar coordinates. We find the solution of the Schrödinger equation

$$\frac{1}{r} \frac{\partial}{\partial r} \left(r \frac{\partial \psi}{\partial r}\right) + \frac{1}{r^2} \frac{\partial^2 \psi}{\partial \varphi^2} + \frac{2m}{\hbar^2} E\psi = 0$$

as a product of two functions

$$\psi(r, \varphi) = f(r)\,\zeta(\varphi).$$

Substituting this last expression in to the Schrödinger equation and denoting by λ^2 the separation constant, we obtain two equations

$$r \frac{\partial}{\partial r} \left(r \frac{\partial f}{\partial r}\right) + r^2\,k^2\,f = \lambda^2\,f, \tag{1}$$

$$\frac{\partial^2 \zeta}{\partial \varphi^2} = -\lambda^2\,\zeta, \tag{2}$$

where $k^2 = 2m\,E/\hbar^2$; m is the mass of the particle and E the kinetic energy.

The solution of equation (2) is at once evident:

$$\zeta(\varphi) = a \sin(\lambda\varphi + \alpha).$$

Since we must have $\zeta(\varphi) = \zeta(\varphi + 2\pi)$ it follows that $\lambda = \pm n$, where $n = 1, 2, 3, \dots$ Equation (1), however, reduces to the Bessel equation. We rewrite it in the following form,

$$r^2 \frac{d^2 f}{dr^2} + r \frac{d f}{dr} + (k^2 r^2 - \lambda^2) f = 0,$$

and then, introducing the new variable $x = kr$ and taking into account that $\lambda^2 = n$, we obtain the standard form of this equation:

$$x^2 \frac{d^2 f}{dx^2} + x \frac{d f}{dx} + (x^2 - n^2) f = 0.$$

Its solutions for integer values of n are nth order Bessel functions $J_n(x)$ of the 1st kind:†

$$f_n(x) = A J_n(x).$$

As an illustration the graph of the first order Bessel function of the first kind, $J_1(x)$, is given in Fig. 45. The solutions obtained should satisfy the boundary condition at the point r_0:

$$f_n(x_i) = 0,$$

where $x_i = k_i r_0$.

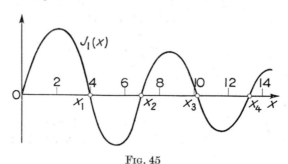

FIG. 45

Thus, for given n (for example $n = 1$) the condition $f_1(x_i) = 0$ is satisfied at the points x_1, x_2, x_3 etc., i.e. for various values of

† See, for example, E. Jahnke and F. Emde, *Tables of Functions*. Dover Publications.

the parameter k_i. Expressing k_i in terms of E, we obtain

$$E_{ni} = \frac{\hbar^2 x_{ni}^2}{2 m\, r_0^2},$$

where the x_{ni} are the zeros of the nth order Bessel function. Thus in the present case one can say that the allowed values of the particle energy are defined by the two quantum numbers n and i.

5.26. (a) $\qquad \alpha = \sqrt{\dfrac{m\,k}{\hbar^2}}, \quad \lambda = \dfrac{2\,E}{\hbar} \sqrt{\dfrac{m}{k}},$

where k is the elastic force modulus and E the total energy of the particle.

(b) $\qquad E_n = \hbar \sqrt{\dfrac{k}{m}} \left(n + \dfrac{1}{2}\right) = \hbar\,\omega_0 \left(n + \dfrac{1}{2}\right),$

where ω_0 is the angular frequency of the oscillator.

5.27. (a) $\qquad \psi_0(\xi) = a_0\, e^{-\xi^2/2},$

$\qquad\qquad\qquad \psi_1(\xi) = 2 a_1\, \xi\, e^{-\xi^2/2},$

$\qquad\qquad\qquad \psi_2(\xi) = 2 a_2 (2\xi^2 - 1)\, e^{-\xi^2/2}$

(b) See Fig. 46, where the shape of the potential well is represented by the broken curve.

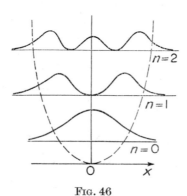

FIG. 46

5.28. $\quad 2 a_0 a_1 \displaystyle\int_{-\infty}^{\infty} \xi e^{-\xi^2}\, d\xi = 0$ since the integrand is odd.

ANP   6a

5.29. $E_0 = \dfrac{\hbar \, \omega_0}{2}$, $E_1 = \dfrac{3}{2} \, \hbar \, \omega_0$,   where $\omega_0 = \sqrt{\dfrac{k}{m}}$,

k is the elastic force modulus and m is the mass of the particle.

5.30. $\psi_0(x) = \sqrt[4]{\dfrac{\alpha^2}{\pi}} \, e^{-\alpha^2 x^2/2}$, $\psi_1(x) = \sqrt{\dfrac{2\alpha^3}{\sqrt{\pi}}} \, x \, e^{-\alpha^2 x^2/2}$

5.31. (a)

$$\bar{x} = 0, \; \bar{x}^2 = \frac{1}{2\alpha^2} = \frac{\hbar}{2 \sqrt{m \, k}} = \frac{E_0}{k}, \; \text{ since } \; \alpha = \sqrt[4]{\frac{m \, k}{\hbar^2}}$$

(see the solution of problem 5.26).

(b) $\bar{x} = 0, \; \bar{x}^2 = \dfrac{3}{2\alpha^2} = \dfrac{3 \hbar}{2 \sqrt{m \, k}} = \dfrac{E_1}{k}.$

Here k is the elastic force modulus and E_0 and E_1 are the energy eigenvalues in the first two states ($n = 0$ and 1).

5.32. The required probability is

$$W = \frac{2 \int\limits_{x_0}^{\infty} \psi_0^2(x) \, dx}{\int\limits_{-\infty}^{\infty} \psi_0^2(x) \, dx} = \frac{\int\limits_{\xi_0}^{\infty} \psi_0^2(\xi) \, d\xi}{\int\limits_{0}^{\infty} \psi_0^2(\xi) \, d\xi},$$

where $\xi = \alpha x$. From the condition that $E_0 = h\nu/2$, we find x_0 and then $\xi_0(\xi_0 = 1)$. Now we have only to represent the integral $\int\limits_1^{\infty}$ in the form $\int\limits_0^{\infty} - \int\limits_0^1$ and then to use the hint given in the problem. Thus we find that $W \approx 0.157$, i.e., 15·7 per cent.

5.33. Substituting the function u directly into the equation $\nabla^2 u = 0$, we obtain an expression, which, when compared with the "angular" equation gives

$$\lambda = l(l + 1) \quad \text{and} \quad L^2 = \hbar^2 \, l \, (l + 1).$$

Thus, angular momentum proves to be quantized.

5.34. Substituting the function $\psi(r) = \dfrac{\chi(r)}{r}$ into the Schrödinger equation, we have

$$\frac{d^2 \chi}{d r^2} + k^2 \chi = 0, \quad \text{where} \quad k = \sqrt{2 m \, E}/\hbar.$$

The general solution of this equation is

$$\chi(r) = a_1 \sin k\,r + a_2 \cos k\,r$$

or

$$\psi(r) = \frac{1}{r}\,(a_1 \sin k\,r + a_2 \cos k\,r).$$

Since $\psi(r)$ is finite for $r = 0$, the coefficient a_2 should be zero. Furthermore, from the boundary condition $\psi(r_0) = 0$ it follows that $k\,r_0 = \pm\,n\,\pi$, $n = 1, 2, 3, \ldots$, or

$$E_n = \frac{\pi^2\,\hbar^2\,n^2}{2\,m\,r_0^2}.$$

5.35. Substituting $\psi(r) = \dfrac{\chi(r)}{r}$ into the Schrödinger equation we find

$$(0 < r < r_0) \quad \frac{d^2\chi_1}{dr^2} + k_1^2\,\chi_1 = 0, \quad \text{where} \quad k_1 = \sqrt{2m\,E}/\hbar,$$

$$(r > r_0) \quad \frac{d^2\chi_2}{dr^2} - k_2^2\,\chi_2 = 0, \quad \text{where} \quad k_2 = \sqrt{2m(U_0 - E)}/\hbar.$$

Hence

$$\chi_1(r) = a_1 \sin k_1\,r + a_2 \cos k_1\,r,$$

$$\chi_2(r) = b\,e^{-k_2 r}.$$

The wave function $\psi(r)$ will be finite in the whole range of r, only if $a_2 = 0$. Since ψ and $d\psi/dr$ are continuous at the point $r = r_0$, we have

$$k_2 \tan k_1\,r_0 = -k_1.$$

As shown in the solution of problem 5.18, this expression defines a discrete energy spectrum.

5.36. (a)

$$\frac{1}{r^2}\left[\frac{\partial}{\partial r}\left(r^2\,\frac{\partial\psi}{\partial r}\right) + \frac{1}{\sin\vartheta}\,\frac{\partial}{\partial\vartheta}\left(\sin\vartheta\,\frac{\partial\psi}{\partial\vartheta}\right) + \frac{1}{\sin^2\vartheta}\,\frac{\partial^2\psi}{\partial\varphi^2}\right]$$

$$+ \frac{2m}{\hbar^2}\left(E + \frac{Z\,e^2}{r}\right)\psi = 0.$$

(b) The variables r and ϑ, φ, can be separated by putting

$$\psi(r, \vartheta, \varphi) = R(r)\,Y(\vartheta, \varphi).$$

Substituting this expression into the Schrödinger equation and denoting the separation constant by λ, we find expressions for the radial and the angular parts:

$$\frac{1}{r^2} \frac{d}{dr}\left(r^2 \frac{dR}{dr}\right) + \left[\frac{2m}{\hbar^2}\left(E + \frac{Ze^2}{r}\right) - \frac{\lambda}{r^2}\right] R = 0,$$

$$\frac{1}{\sin\vartheta} \frac{\partial}{\partial\vartheta}\left(\sin\vartheta \frac{\partial Y}{\partial\vartheta}\right) + \frac{1}{\sin^2\vartheta} \frac{\partial^2 Y}{\partial\varphi^2} + \lambda Y = 0.$$

(c) In the angle equation the variables ϑ and φ can also be separated by putting $Y(\vartheta, \varphi) = \theta(\vartheta)\Phi(\varphi)$. Denoting the separation constant by $\varkappa^2$, we find the equation defining $\Phi(\varphi)$ to be:

$$\frac{d^2\Phi}{d\varphi^2} + \varkappa^2\Phi = 0,$$

hence
$$\Phi(\varphi) = a\, e^{i\varkappa\varphi}.$$

From the requirement of single valuedness $\Phi(\varphi) = \Phi(\varphi + 2\pi)$ it follows that $\varkappa = m$, where $m = 0, \pm 1, \pm 2, \ldots$ (the magnetic quantum number). Hence

$$\psi(r, \vartheta, \varphi) = R(r)\,\theta(\vartheta)\, e^{im\varphi}.$$

5.37. (a) Substituting $\chi(r) = rR(r)$ we reduce the given equation to the asymptotic form†

$$\frac{d^2\chi}{dr^2} + \frac{2m}{\hbar^2} E\chi = 0,$$

whence
$$\chi(r) = a_1 e^{ikr} + a_2{}^{-ikr}, \quad \text{where} \quad k = \sqrt{2mE}/\hbar,$$

or
$$R(r) = \frac{1}{r}(a_1 e^{ikr} + a_2 e^{-ikr}).$$

For $E > 0$ the solution remains finite for large values of r. Hence it follows that the spectrum of E is continuous in the region $E > 0$. For $E < 0$ the solution remains finite only when $a_2 = 0$. Hence

$$R(r) = \frac{a_1}{r} e^{-kr},$$

where
$$k = \sqrt{2m\,|\,E\,|}/\hbar.$$

---

† The neglect of $\dfrac{\chi}{r}$ by comparison with $\dfrac{d^2\chi}{dr^2}$ is not strictly allowable.[3] However, the above treatment is correct if the Coulomb field is screened at large distances.

(b) Making the substitution $\chi = rR$ and using the fact that $\lambda = l(l + 1)$ we obtain the equation

$$\frac{d^2\chi}{dr^2} = l(l + 1)\frac{\chi}{r^2},$$

which is valid for small values of r. It is immediately evident that the solution of this equation should be sought in the form $\chi = ar^\alpha$, Hence we find that $\alpha = l + 1$ and -1. The function $R(r)$ is finite only when α has the first of these two values, so that

$$R(r) = a\, r^l.$$

5.38. Substituting the solution given into the Schrödinger equation we find

$$r\left(\alpha^2 + \frac{2m}{\hbar^2}E_1\right) + \left(\frac{2m\,e^2}{\hbar^2} - 2\alpha\right) = 0.$$

In order that this equality should be valid for all values of r, the coefficients of r and l must be separately equated to zero, whence

$$E_1 = -\frac{m\,e^4}{2\hbar^2}.$$

As may be easily seen this expression is identical with the expression for the energy of the first Bohr orbit of the atom.

5.39. (a) $W(r)dr = \psi^2\,dv$, where the volume of the spherical shell between r and $r + dr$, i.e. $4\pi r^2\,dr$, is taken as the volume element. Then

$$W(r)\,dr = 4\pi\,a^2\,r^2\,e^{-2r/r_1}\,dr.$$

(b) $W(r)$ has a maximum for $r = r_1$.

(c) See Fig. 47.

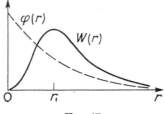

Fig. 47

5.40. Taking into account that $W(r)\,\mathrm{d}r \sim 4\pi r^2 R^2(r)\,\mathrm{d}r$, we find that

$$r_{2p} = 4r_1 \quad \text{and} \quad r_{3d} = 9r_1.$$

5.41. $2s$, $2p$; $3s$, $3p$, $3d$; $-3{\cdot}4$ and $-1{\cdot}51$ eV.

5.42. $\Delta_1\psi + \Delta_2\psi + \dfrac{2m}{\hbar^2}\left(E + \dfrac{2e^2}{r_1} + \dfrac{2e^2}{r_2} - \dfrac{e^2}{r_{12}}\right)\,\psi = 0,$

where ∇_1^2 and ∇_2^2 are Laplace operators acting on the coordinates of the first and the second electron which are at distances r_1 and r_2 respectively from the nucleus, and r_{12} is the distance between the electrons.

5.43.

$$\Delta_1\psi + \Delta_2\psi + \frac{2m}{\hbar^2}\left(E + \frac{e^2}{r_{1a}} + \frac{e^2}{r_{2a}} + \frac{e^2}{r_{1b}} + \frac{e^2}{r_{2b}} - \frac{e^2}{r_{12}} - \frac{e^2}{r_{ab}}\right)$$
$$\times\,\psi = 0,$$

where ∇_1^2 and ∇_2^2 are the Laplace operators acting on the coordinates of the first and the second electron; the rest of the notation is evident from Fig. 48, where the nuclei of the molecule are marked A and B, and the electrons marked e.

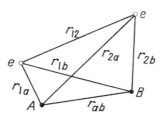

FIG. 48

5.44. Let us write down the Schrödinger equation for the regions to the left and to the right of the point $x = 0$:

$$(x < 0)\ \psi_1'' + k_1^2\psi^2 = 0, \quad \text{where}\quad k_1 = \sqrt{2m\,E}/\hbar,$$
$$(x > 0)\ \psi_2'' + k_2^2\psi_2 = 0, \quad \text{where}\quad k_2 = \sqrt{2m(E - U_0)}/\hbar.$$

Their general solutions are:

$$\psi_1 = a_1\, e^{ik_1 x} + a_2\, e^{-ik_1 x},$$
$$\psi_2 = b_1\, e^{ik_2 x} + b_2\, e^{-ik_2 x}.$$

The wave function should be smooth and continuous in all space; for this to be so, it is necessary that

$$\psi_1(0) = \psi_2(0),$$
$$\psi_1'(0) = \psi_2'(0),$$

or

$$a_1 + a_2 = b_1 + b_2,$$
$$k_1(a_1 - a_2) = k_2(b_1 - b_2).$$

The reflection coefficient R is the ratio of the probability densities of the reflected beam of particles and the incident beam, or, in other words, to the ratio of the squared amplitudes of reflected and incoming waves.

We shall assume that the incoming wave, i.e. that moving to the right, has an amplitude a_1, and the reflected one an amplitude a_2. Then, evidently, $b_2 = 0$, since in the region where $x > 0$, there is only a transmitted wave.† Also, for simplicity we shall consider that the amplitude a_1 is real.

From the last two equations we find a_2/a_1 and obtain:

$$R = \left| \frac{a_2}{a_1} \right|^2 = \left(\frac{k_1 - k_2}{k_1 + k_2} \right)^2 = \left(\frac{1 - \sqrt{1 - \dfrac{U_0}{E}}}{1 + \sqrt{1 - \dfrac{U_0}{E}}} \right)^2.$$

The "transparency" coefficient D represents the probability that the particle will pass through the potential barrier. It can be easily found from the condition that the total probability is 1: the particle will either be reflected or will pass through the barrier. Hence

$$D = 1 - R = \frac{4\sqrt{1 - \dfrac{U_0}{E}}}{\left(1 + \sqrt{1 - \dfrac{U_0}{E}} \right)^2}.$$

† We can equally assume that a_2 is the amplitude of the incoming and a_1 the amplitude of the reflected wave: it all depends on which factor $e^{i\omega t}$ or $e^{-i\omega t}$ is used in the final solution. The arbitrary choice allowed here evidently does not affect the physical meaning of the solution.

5.45. From the Schrödinger equation it follows that the wave functions in the regions to the left and to the right of the point $x = 0$ are of the following form:

$$\psi_1(x < 0) = a_1 e^{ik_1x} + a_2 e^{-ik_1x}, \quad k_1 = \sqrt{2mE}/\hbar.$$

$$\psi_2(x > 0) = b_1 e^{k_2x} + b_2 e^{-k_2x}, \quad k_2 = \sqrt{2m(U_0 - E)}/\hbar,$$

The wave function should be finite everywhere and hence we must have that $b_1 = 0$. Also since ψ and $d\psi/dx$ must be continuous at the point $x = 0$, we have that

$$a_1 + a_2 = b_2,$$

$$i k_1(a_1 - a_2) = -k_2 b_2.$$

To determine the transparency coefficient D of the barrier, we use the fact that the sum of the probabilities of the particle being reflected from the barrier (R) or being transmitted through it (D) is evidently equal to 1. Hence

$$D = 1 - R.$$

The reflection coefficient R is equal to the ratio of the squares of the amplitudes of the reflected and the incoming waves. Putting a_1 and a_2 respectively for the amplitudes of the incoming and the reflected waves (see footnote on page 165), and assuming also for simplicity that a_1 is real, from the above boundary conditions we find that:

$$D = 1 - \left| \frac{a_2}{a_1} \right|^2 = 1 - \left| \frac{i k_1 + k_2}{i k_1 - k_2} \right|^2 = 0.$$

The probability density for finding the particle in the region of positive x, where $U_0 > E$, is found in the usual way:

$$W(x) = \psi_2^2 = a_2^2 e^{-\frac{2}{\hbar} \sqrt{2m(U_0 - E)}x}.$$

From the form of the function $W(x)$ and the fact that $D = 0$ we can conclude that the particle only "dips into" the region where $x > 0$, and, after being "reflected", turns back.

5.46. Let us write down the Schrödinger equation for the three regions

$$(x < 0) \quad \psi_1'' + k_1^2 \psi_1 = 0,$$

$$(0 < x < l) \quad \psi_2'' - k_2^2 \psi_2 = 0,$$

$$(x > l) \quad \psi_3'' + k_1^2 \psi_3 = 0,$$

where

$$k_1 = \sqrt{2m\,E}/\hbar,\ k_2 = \sqrt{2m(U_0 - E)}/\hbar.$$

Their general solutions are:

$$\psi_1 = a_1\,e^{ik_1 x} + a_2\,e^{-ik_1 x},$$

$$\psi_2 = b_1\,e^{k_2 x} + b_2\,e^{-k_2 x},$$

$$\psi_3 = c_1\,e^{ik_1 x} + c_2\,e^{-ik_1 x}.$$

We shall assume for simplicity that the amplitude a_1 of the incoming wave is real.

The "transparency" coefficient D is in this case simply equal to the squared modulus of the amplitude ratio of the transmitted and the incoming waves, i.e., to $|c_1/a_1|^2$. To obtain D we use the boundary conditions, which require that the wave function and its derivative must be continuous at the points $x = 0$ and $x = l$, whence it follows that:

$$a_1 + a_2 = b_1 + b_2,$$

$$i\,k_1(a_1 - a_2) = k_2(b_1 - b_2),$$

$$b_1\,e^{k_2 l} + b_2\,e^{-k_2 l} = c_1\,e^{ik_1 l},$$

$$k_2(b_1\,e^{k_2 l} - b_2\,e^{-k_2 l}) = i\,k_1 c_1\,e^{ik_1 l}.$$

Here we have taken into account that the amplitude c_2, which corresponds to the wave moving to the left, is zero.

Solving these equations we find

$$\frac{c_1}{a_1} = \frac{4\,k_1\,k_2\,e^{-ik_1 l}}{(k_1 - i\,k_2)^2\,e^{-k_2 l} - (k_1 + i\,k_2)^2\,e^{k_2 l}}.$$

And finally:

$$D = \left|\frac{c_1}{a_1}\right|^2 = \frac{1}{\left(\dfrac{k_1^2 + k_2^2}{2\,k_1\,k_2}\right)^2 \sinh^2(k_2\,l) + 1},$$

where sinh is the hyperbolic sine

$$\left(\sinh x = \frac{e^x - e^{-x}}{2}\right).$$

For the practically interesting cases when $k_2 l$ is of the order of several units, we have $\sinh^2(k_2 l) \approx e^{2k_2 l}$. Then, with sufficient approximation we find that

$$D = A\, e^{-\frac{2}{\hbar}\sqrt{2m\,(U_0-E)}\,l}$$

where A is a certain constant, approximately equal to 1.

5.47. See answer to 5.46.

5.48. $D \approx e^{\frac{4\sqrt{2m}}{3\hbar e E}(U_0-E)^{3/2}} \approx \begin{cases} 0\cdot001 & (E = E_1), \\ 0\cdot032 & (E = E_2). \end{cases}$

CHAPTER 6

6.1. 43,500; 41,400; 35,000; 33,700 and 31,400 cm^{-1}.

6.2. (a) $\sigma_s = -0.4$; $\sigma_p = -0.04$; σ_d and σ_f differ little from zero.

(b) The d and f terms, for which the field is almost of pure Coulomb character.

6.3. 3230, 6720, 8170 and 26,250 Å.

6.4. *Hint:* make use of diagram in Fig. 2.5.

6.5. 5890 and 11,400 Å.

6.6. $\sigma_s = -2.23$; $\sigma_p = -1.915$.

6.7. $a_s = 9.16$; $a_p = 9.57$; $a_d = 9.997$.

6.8. $n = 2$, $\alpha = 1.76$. See Fig. 49.

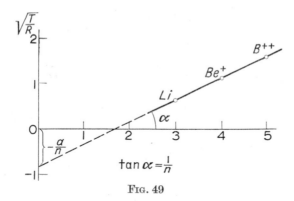

FIG. 49

6.9. The doublet character of the alkali metals spectra; the complicated splitting of spectral lines in a magnetic field (the anomalous Zeeman effect); the splitting of a beam of alkali atoms, all in the ground state, when passing through a transverse inhomogeneous magnetic field (the Stern–Gerlach experiment); the gyromagnetic effects (the experiments of Barnett and of Einstein and de Haas) etc.

6.10. See Reference 2.

6.11. The maximum interaction energy corresponds to the case when the spin magnetic moment and the orbital magnetic moment are parallel. Then

$$E_{\max} \sim \frac{\mu_0^2}{r_1^3} = 3 \cdot 6 \times 10^{-4} \, \text{eV},$$

where μ_0 is the Bohr magneton and r_1 the radius of the first Bohr orbit.

6.12. In order that the correction term in the fine structure formula be zero it is necessary that

$$\frac{1}{j + \frac{1}{2}} - \frac{3}{4n} = 0,$$

or

$$j = \frac{4}{3} n - \frac{1}{2}.$$

It can easily be shown that the latter relation cannot be satisfied for any possible values of n and j. Actually:

$$n = l_{\max} + 1 = j_{\max} + \frac{1}{2}.$$

Let us substitute the last expression into the preceding one:

$$j = \frac{4}{3} \left(j_{\max} + \frac{1}{2} \right) - \frac{1}{2} > j_{\max}!$$

The absurdity of the result obtained proves our statement.

6.13. Schrödinger's equation was set up so as to yield the classical mechanics of point particles in the limit $\hbar \to 0$, according to the requirements of the correspondence principle. Spin represents additional degrees of freedom of the particles which are of a quantum nature. Their relation to the requirements of special relativity is obtained by the use of the Dirac equation.

6.14. $$\Delta \lambda = \frac{\alpha^2}{9R} = 0 \cdot 0054 \, \text{Å},$$

where α is the fine structure constant.

6.15. The intervals are $1 \cdot 734$ and $0 \cdot 577 \, \text{cm}^{-1}$.

6.16. Figure 50 shows the scheme of terms and of allowed transitions that satisfy the selections rules for the quantum numbers l and j.

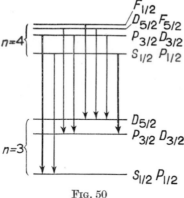

FIG. 50

The transitions which correspond to the end components of multiplets are represented by heavy lines. From the difference in the wave numbers of these we have that

$$\Delta \lambda = \frac{\Delta \bar{\nu}}{\bar{\nu}^2} = 0.54 \text{ Å}.$$

6.17. The origin of fine structure lies in the existence of spin–orbit coupling. For s-waves ($l = 0$) this is absent.

6.18. Yes.

6.19. 63·2 per cent.

6.20. Let τ be the mean lifetime of an atom in an excited state. Then each atom emits on the average $1/\tau$ quanta every second and the total radiative power of N atoms is

$$W = \frac{1}{\tau} N h \nu.$$

Here $N = \dfrac{g}{g_0} N_0 \, e^{-h\nu/kT}$, g/g_0 is the ratio of the statistical weights (the degrees of degeneracy) of the resonance and the ground energy levels, and N_0 is the number of atoms in the ground state.

By direct calculation we find that, under the conditions given, $N \ll N_0$. This permits us to assume with sufficient accuracy that N_0 is the number of all atoms in the given volume:

$$N_0 = p \, v/kT.$$

As a result we find

$$\tau = \frac{h\,c\,p\,v}{k\,T\,\lambda\,W}\,\frac{g}{g_0}\,e^{-hc/kT\lambda} = 2 \times 10^{-8}\ \text{sec}.$$

6.21. $\tau = 1\cdot25 \times 10^{-6}$ sec.

6.22. These factors are: the Doppler effect, the finite life-time of an atom in an excited state due to spontaneous emission of photons, the interatomic interactions leading to pressure broadening (as the pressure of the radiating gas increases, the width of the spectral lines also increases).

6.23.
$$\frac{\Delta\lambda_g}{\Delta\lambda_e} = \frac{4\pi\tau}{\lambda}\sqrt{\frac{2RT}{\mu}} = 770.$$

6.24.
$$\alpha = \frac{\lambda}{2\pi\,\eta\,\tau\,v} = 2'.$$

6.25. $4 : 1$.

6.26.
$$T = \frac{h\,c\,(\lambda_1 - \lambda_2)}{k\,\lambda_1\,\lambda_2\,\ln\left(\dfrac{g_2}{g_1}\dfrac{J_1}{J_2}\right)} = 2770°\text{K}.$$

Here J_1/J_2 is the intensity ratio of the components of the line, g_1 and g_2 are the statistical weights (the degrees of degeneracy) of the corresponding excited sublevels.

6.27. (a) $2 : 1$.

(b) $\dfrac{\Delta\,(J_1/J_2)}{J_1/J_2}\,1 - e^{-(E_1 - E_2)/kT} = \begin{cases} 1.2\ \text{per cent for sodium}, \\ 6.3\ \text{per cent for potassium}. \end{cases}$

7.1. 3, 2, 1; respectively $\hbar\sqrt{12}$, $\hbar\sqrt{6}$ and $\hbar\sqrt{2}$.

7.2. (a) $110°\,45'$;

(b) $45°$;

(c) $160°\,35'$.

7.3. $\dfrac{\hbar\sqrt{35}}{2}$ and $\dfrac{\hbar\sqrt{15}}{2}$ respectively $61°\,50'$ and $135°$.

7.4. $S = {}^3/_2 : J = {}^3/_2, {}^5/_2, {}^7/_2, {}^9/_2$; $S = 2 : J = 1, 2, 3, 4, 5$; $S = {}^5/_2 : J = {}^1/_2, {}^3/_2, {}^5/_2, {}^7/_2, {}^9/_2, {}^{11}/_2$; $S = 4 : J = 1, 2, 3, 4, 5, 6, 7$.

7.5. For $L = S$ the number of possible values of J is determined by either one of the two expressions.

7.6. In this notation the term symbol ${}^{2S+1}L_j$ always gives the complete set of quantum numbers L, S and J.

7.7. Using an L–S coupling scheme we may have $S = 0$ or 1, hence singlets or triplets.

7.8. The sets of terms characteristic of the two types of coupling will be different, leading to a different grouping of multiplets.

7.9. The singlet terms are ${}^1P_1$, ${}^1D_2$ and ${}^1F_3$.
The triplets are ${}^3P_0$, ${}^3P_1$, ${}^3P_2$; ${}^3D_1$, ${}^2D_2$, ${}^3D_3$; ${}^3F_2$, ${}^3F_3$, ${}^3F_4$.

7.10. Note that when a photon is emitted the total angular momentum of the atom p_J changes vectorially. Hence one sees easily that the condition $\Delta J = 0$ corresponds to the case when p_J changes only in direction and not in magnitude.

7.11. $2\sqrt{3}\,\mu_0$ where μ_0 is the Bohr magneton. The values of the projections (in Bohr magnetons) are: 3, 2, 1, 0, -1, -2, -3.

7.12. $2\cdot58 \times 10^{-4}$ and $1\cdot29 \times 10^{-2}\,\mathrm{eV}$.

7.13. $2\,(S)$; ${}^2/_3$ and ${}^4/_3\,(P)$; ${}^4/_5$ and ${}^6/_5\,(D)$.

7.14. $\dfrac{0}{0}\,({}^3P_0)$, ${}^3/_2\,({}^3P_1)$, ${}^3/_2\,({}^3P_2)$.

7.15. The total magnetic moment of the atom is:

$$\mu_J = \mu_0\sqrt{2S(S+1) + 2J(J+1) - L(L+1)} = 3\cdot74\,\mu_0.$$

The effective magnetic moment is:

$$\mu = g\,\mu_0\,\sqrt{J(J+1)} = 3.67\mu_0.$$

Here μ_0 is the Bohr magneton, g the Landé factor; S, J and L are the quantum numbers that describe the given state of the atom.

7.16. For both terms the Landé factor is zero.

According to the vector model of the atom, this means that the vector of the magnetic moment of an atom is perpendicular to the vector of its total angular momentum. This can be easily seen by direct calculation and even more simply from a graphical representation of the vector model of the atom (Fig. 51).

7.17. From the relation given in the problem it follows that

$$\mathrm{d}\mathbf{P} = \mathbf{M}\,\mathrm{d}t = [\boldsymbol{\mu}\,\mathbf{H}]\,\mathrm{d}t,$$

where $\boldsymbol{\mu}$ is the magnetic moment of the atom.

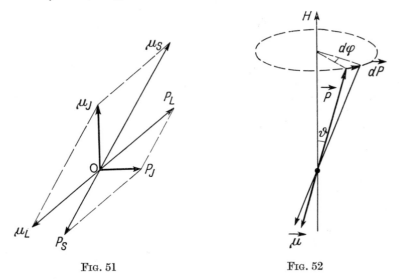

FIG. 51   FIG. 52

On the other hand, $\mathrm{d}P$ can be expressed by geometrical reasoning (see Fig. 52) as

$$\mathrm{d}P = P\sin\vartheta\,\mathrm{d}\varphi = P\sin\vartheta\,\omega\,\mathrm{d}t,$$

where ω is the rotational angular velocity of the vector $\mathbf{P}$ about the direction of the magnetic field $\mathbf{H}$.

Comparing the above expressions we obtain:

$$\omega = \frac{\mu}{P} H = \frac{e}{2 m c} H, \quad e > 0.$$

7.18. (a) $7 \times 10^5 \sec^{-1}$;
   (b) $7 \times 10^{11} \sec^{-1}$.

7.19. $8 \cdot 8 \times 10^8$ rad/sec (^1P); $1 \cdot 76 \times 10^9$ rad/sec $(^2S_{1/2})$ and
$1 \cdot 17 \times 10^9$ rad/sec $(^2P_{3/2})$.

7.20. $\Delta E = \mu H (1 - \cos \vartheta) = g \mu_0 H \left(\sqrt{J(J+1)} - J \right)$,

where μ is the effective magnetic moment of the atom, ϑ the angle
between the magnetic moment of the atom and the vector **H** and
μ_0 the Bohr magneton.
The Landé factor g is found from the condition

$$\omega_L = g \frac{e}{2 m c} H;$$

then, knowing g, L and S, we find J. Thus we obtain

$$\Delta E = 1 \cdot 72 \times 10^{-6} \text{ eV}.$$

7.21. For singlet lines that arise as the result of transitions
between terms whose spin is zero we have: $^1F_3 \to {}^1D_2$.

7.22. The selection rule $\Delta m_L = 0$, ± 1 results in three lines only
occurring.

7.23. The motion of an electron in an atom can be represented
generally in the form of three mutually perpendicular harmonic
oscillations. To simplify the argument we shall represent oscillations in a plane perpendicular to the direction of the magnetic
field as circular motions.
  It is known that an electric dipole does not radiate along the
direction of the dipole itself. We know also that the revolution
frequency of electrons for which $\omega \uparrow\uparrow$ **H** increases in the magnetic
field, while the revolution frequency of electrons with $\omega \uparrow\downarrow$ **H**
decreases.
  These arguments and Fig. 53, allow us to explain easily why in
the normal Zeeman effect in the direction perpendicular to the
field the splitting of the spectral lines is observed to be into three
components and that in the parallel direction into two.

7.24. $\Delta \bar{\nu} = \dfrac{e\,H}{\pi\,m\,c^2} = 9{\cdot}32 \text{ cm}^{-1}; \quad 1{\cdot}16 \times 10^{-3}\,\text{eV}.$

7.25. We find the orbital quantum number from the formula

$$L = \frac{2\pi\,m\,c^2\,\Delta T}{e\,\Delta H} = 3.$$

Here m and e are the mass and the charge of the electron respectively and c the velocity of light. Hence the term symbol is $^1F_3$.

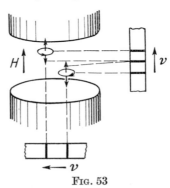

$H\uparrow$ $\uparrow \nu$

$\longleftarrow \nu$

FIG. 53

7.26. $A = \dfrac{\lambda}{\Delta \lambda} = \dfrac{2\pi\,m\,c^2}{e\,H\,\lambda} = 10^5,$

$N = 5 \times 10^4$ lines (since $A = kN$, where k is the order of the spectrum).

7.27. This is due to Planck's constant "accidentally" dropping out of the formulae.

7.28. Gases that consist of atoms with an odd number of electrons will show only the anomalous Zeeman effect, while those whose atoms contain an even number of electrons will show both the normal (in singlet lines) and the anomalous effects (in lines of other multiplicities).

7.29. The normal effect occurs only for the first line.

7.30. (a) The magnitude of the natural splitting is $1{\cdot}35$ cm^{-1}; the Zeeman splitting in the given field is $0{\cdot}312$ cm^{-1}.

   (b) Yes.

7.31. Both questions can be easily answered by looking at Fig. 54. Here the transitions that differ most from each other are drawn as heavy lines. They represent the end components of the multiplet. One must also take into account that the intervals between the top terms are $\sim g_2$, and those between the lower ones $\sim g_1$.

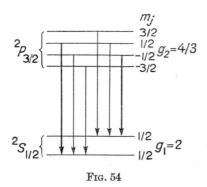

FIG. 54

(a) 6 components;

(b) $$\Delta \bar{\nu} = (g_1 + g_2) \frac{e\,H}{4\pi\,m\,c^2} = 0.156 \text{ cm}^{-1}.$$

7.32. $$H = \frac{3h\,c\,\Delta\lambda}{7\mu_0\,\lambda^2} \approx 1.58 \times 10^5 \text{ oe}.$$

Here $\Delta\lambda$ is the wavelength interval between the two components of a doublet line, λ the average wavelength of a doublet and μ_0 the Bohr magneton.

7.33. n, l, j, m_j in a "weak" field; n, l, m_l, m_s in a "strong" field.

7.34. It is evident from Fig. 55 that in the weak field there arise $4 + 6 = 10$ components and in a strong one, as in the normal Zeeman effect, only three.

7.35. In a "strong" magnetic field the L–S coupling is not completely destroyed. There remains a weak interaction and it appears in the form of the fine structure of the triplet components, (Fig. 55).

7.36. (a) In an inhomogeneous magnetic field atoms with magnetic moments different from zero will not only process about the direction of the field, but will also deviate from their original direction of motion.

(b) In the direction of increasing magnetic field strength.

7.37. (a) The electron has to be associated with a sufficiently large mass, to make perturbations due to the apparatus less noticeable. Otherwise the wave character of its motion (the un-

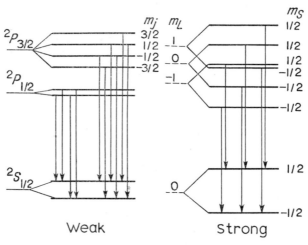

FIG. 55

certainty relation) under the conditions of the Stern–Gerlach experiment will completely hide the desired effect.

The ground states of the atoms in the first group of the periodic table are S states ($L = 0$) and therefore the total angular momentum of the atom coincides with its spin angular momentum.

(b) The magnetic moment of a nucleus due to its spin is considerably smaller on account of the larger mass of the nucleus, hence the interaction with the external magnetic field is practically determined entirely by the spin of the electron.

7.38.
$$\mu_H = \frac{m\,v^2\,\Delta\,l}{l_1(l_1 + 2l_2)\dfrac{\partial H}{\partial z}} = 0.93 \times 10^{-20}\ \text{erg/gauss},$$

where m is the mass of the atom.

7.39.
$$f = \frac{3kT\,\Delta\,l}{l_1(l_1 + 2l_2)} = 8.3 \times 10^{-16}\,d,$$

where k is Boltzmann's constant.

7.40. Let us define $\mu_{H\max}$ from the expression

$$\mu_{H\max} = g\,\mu_0 J,$$

where g is the Landé factor, μ_0 the Bohr magneton and J the intrinsic quantum number ($J = m_{J\max}$). We can find the quantum number S from the multiplicity of the terms, the value of which is fixed by the expression $2S + 1$. The number of components of the beam is equal to $2J + 1$, whence we find J. After calculating the g factors we obtain the following values for $\mu_{H\max}$ in Bohr magnetons: 0·6 for vanadium, 5 for manganese, 6 for iron.

7.41.
$$\Delta l = \frac{g\,\mu_0\,J\,l_1(l_1 + 2\,l_2)\dfrac{\partial H}{\partial z}}{m\,v^2} = 2\cdot83\,\text{mm},$$

where g is the Landé factor, μ_0 the Bohr magneton, J the intrinsic quantum number of the atom and m its mass.

7.42. The first field splits the beam into $2J + 1$ components; the second, perpendicular to the first, splits each of these again, into $2J + 1$ components. Consequently the original beam is split into $(2J + 1)^2$ components.

CHAPTER 8

8.1. See answer to 8.5.

8.2. (a) He, Be and C are diamagnetic, the others are para-magnetic.

(b) In the metallic state, chemical binding occurs leading to effective canellation of the electron spins.

8.3. $-1\cdot4 \times 10^{-6}$ erg/gauss² mole.

8.4.
$$\bar{\mu} = \frac{1-\mu}{4\pi} \frac{A'}{N\cdot\varrho} H = \begin{cases} \text{(copper)} \\ \text{(bismuth)} \end{cases}$$

Here A is the atomic weight, μ the magnetic permeability, N Avogadro's number, ϱ the density of the diamagnetic material and μ_0 the Bohr magneton.

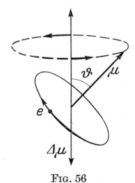

FIG. 56

8.5. An electron moving with a high velocity about a nucleus can be considered as uniformly "smeared" over the orbit (Fig. 56). Then, as a result of Larmor precession, an element of the orbit of charge de and mass dm will generate an induced magnetic moment:

$$d\mu = \frac{de}{2c\,dm}\,dp,$$

180

where dp is the corresponding angular momentum. Evidently $dp = dm \cdot \omega_L r^2$, where ω_L is the Larmor angular velocity of precession and r the distance from the element dm to the precession axis. Thus

$$d\mu = \frac{de}{2c} r^2 \omega_L.$$

Integrating this expression over all elements of the orbit, we get:

$$\Delta \mu = \frac{\omega_L}{2c} \int r^2 \, de,$$

and taking the average over all possible orientations of the orbits of different atoms, we have

$$\overline{\Delta \mu} = \frac{\omega_L}{2c} \int \overline{r^2} \, de.$$

In a cartesian coordinate system, with its origin in the centre of the atom and its z-axis coincident with the vector $\mathbf{H}$, we have for every element of the orbit

$$x^2 + y^2 + z^2 = r_0^2,$$

where r_0 is the orbit radius. If the orbits are orientated completely at random, we have evidently

$$\bar{x}^2 = \bar{y}^2 = \bar{z}^2 = \frac{1}{3} r_0^2 \quad \text{and}$$

$$\bar{r}^2 = \bar{x}^2 + \bar{y}^2 = \frac{2}{3} r_0^2.$$

Taking into account also that $\omega_L = eH/2mc$, we have finally

$$\overline{\Delta \mu} = \frac{e^2 r_0^2 H}{6m c^2} = 2 \cdot 6 \times 10^{-27} \text{ erg/gauss.}$$

8.6. 0·45 erg deg/gauss^2 mole; 1·76 $\times$ 10^{-20} erg/gauss.

8.7. $$\mu = \sqrt{\frac{3kT I}{N H}} = 0 \cdot 225 \mu_0,$$

where N is Avogadro's number and μ_0 the Bohr magneton.

8.8. By 1·6 $\times$ 10^{-6}.

8.9. (a) 0·7 erg/gauss, 1·6 $\times$ 10^{-5} erg/gauss,

(b) 7 $\times$ 10^{-5} erg/gauss.

8.10. By 88 per cent.

8.11. $\qquad \bar{\mu} = \mu\left(\cot a - \dfrac{1}{a}\right)$, where $a = \dfrac{\mu H}{kT}$.

8.12. (a) $\qquad \bar{\mu}_H = \begin{cases} \dfrac{\mu^2 H}{3kT} \text{ ("weak" field)}, \\[2mm] \mu \quad \text{("strong" field)}. \end{cases}$

(b) $1\cdot 12 \times 10^{-3}\,\mu_0$ and $0\cdot 04\,\mu_0$, where μ_0 is the Bohr magneton.

8.13. $\qquad f = \mu\left(\cot a - \dfrac{1}{a}\right)\dfrac{\partial H}{\partial x}\dfrac{N\,p}{RT} = 2\cdot 5\,\text{g}.$

Here $a = \mu H/kT$, N is Avogadro's number, p the pressure, R the universal gas constant and T the absolute temperature.

8.14. See Fig. 57. Here $L(a)$ is the Langevin function

$$L(a) = \cot a - \frac{1}{a}.$$

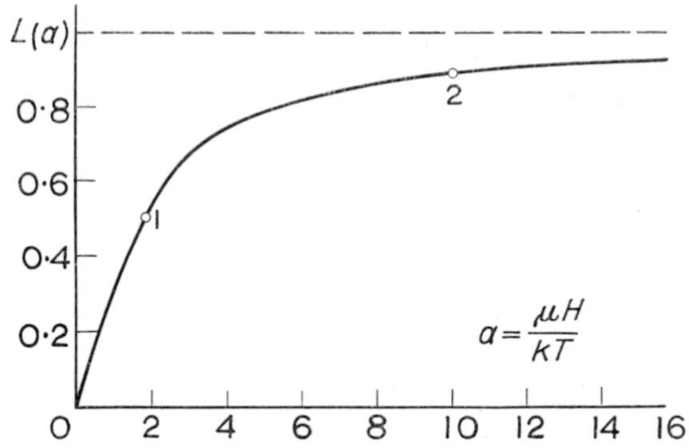

FIG. 57

At the points 1 and 2 the intensity of the magnetic field is 8 and 45 Moe respectively.

8.15. By definition of the mean value we have:

$$\bar{\mu}_H = \frac{\sum \mu_H\,e^{\mu H/kT}}{\sum e^{\mu H/kT}} = \frac{g\,\mu_0\displaystyle\sum_{m=-j}^{+j} m\,e^{\alpha m}}{\displaystyle\sum_{m=-j}^{+j} e^{\alpha m}},$$

where g is the Landé factor, m the magnetic quantum number, μ_0 the Bohr magneton, and

$$\alpha = \frac{g\,\mu_0\,H}{k\,T}.$$

In calculating the sums in the numerator and the denominator, we use the smallness of the parameter α ($\alpha \ll 1$ for a "weak" magnetic field), which permits us to replace the function $e^{\alpha m}$ sufficiently accurately by the first two terms of its expansion in a series:

$$e^{\alpha m} \approx 1 + \alpha\,m.$$

Then

$$\sum_{m=-j}^{+j} m\,e^{\alpha m} = \sum_{m=-j}^{+j} m\,(1 + \alpha\,m) = \alpha \sum_{m=-j}^{+j} m^2 = \alpha\frac{j\,(j+1)\,(2j+1)}{3}$$

and

$$\sum_{m=-j}^{+j} e^{\alpha m} = \sum_{m=-j}^{+j} (1 + \alpha\,m) = 2j + 1.$$

After substituting the expression obtained into the original formula, we find:

$$\bar{\mu}_H = \frac{\mu_0^2\,g^2\,j\,(j+1)\,H}{3\,k\,T}.$$

8.16. $\dfrac{N_+}{N_-}\,e^{2jg\mu_0 H/kT} = 1{\cdot}013.$

8.17. $0{\cdot}179$ erg/gauss.

8.18. $1{\cdot}25 \times 10^{-3}$ erg/gauss.

8.19. $0{\cdot}389$ erg/gauss.

8.20. In the case of the rare earth elements, even for the condensed state, the effect of chemical binding is not large, since the paramagnetism of these atoms is caused by the inner electrons which are strongly screened, leading to very little overlap of these electrons.

8.21. (a) In a "strong" constant field **H** the magnetic moments μ of the atoms (or molecules) of substances are orientated in a completely definite way with respect to the direction of **H** (spatial quantization). Each orientation of μ corresponds to a definite value of the energy $\mu_H\,H$. A transition from one energy state to another (a change in the orientation of μ) can occur only as a consequence of absorption of a quantum of energy from the variable field equal in magnitude to the energy difference of the two states. Thus

$$h\,v = (\mu_H' - \mu_H'')\,H\,,$$

where $\mu_H = g\mu_0 m$ and m is the magnetic quantum number.

(b) Taking into account the selection rules for $m\,(\varDelta m = \pm 1)$, we have:

$$h\,v = g\,\mu_0\,H\,.$$

8.22. $1 \cdot 87 \times 10^9$ c/s.

CHAPTER 9

9.1. 34·3 cm.

9.2. 10^{-4} and 0·2 cm^{-1}.

9.3. (a) 0·1 mm, (b) 1·153.

9.4. In X-ray scattering the X-ray photon is deflected from its path (with some change of frequency). In absorption, the photon energy is transferred to a secondary electron or to creation of an electron–positron pair $(E > 1 \text{ MeV})$.

9.5. $Z = \dfrac{3 \dfrac{\sigma}{\varrho} m^2 c^4 A}{8\pi e^4 N}$, whence we have, respectively 7, 8, 9.

Here σ/ϱ is the mass scattering coefficient, A the atomic weight, and N Avogadro's number.

9.6. $6·57 \times 10^{-25}$ cm^2. "Classical" radius r_0 given by $e^2/r_0 = mc^2$ whence $r_0 = 2·93 \times 10^{-12}$.

9.7. $\tau_\alpha = 1·17 \times 10^{-22}$ cm^2.

9.8. When X-rays pass through compounds the additivity law for absorption is valid: the atoms of each element absorb X-rays independently of the presence of atoms of other elements. Hence

$$\frac{\tau}{\varrho} = \sum_i \left(\frac{\tau}{\varrho}\right)_i \eta_i,$$

where η_i is the weight fraction of the element i in the compound material. Therefore we have

$$\frac{(\tau/\varrho)_{\text{bone}}}{(\tau/\varrho)_{\text{tissue}}} = 8·7.$$

9.9. (a) $\quad d = \dfrac{\ln n}{\varrho\left[\left(\dfrac{\mu}{\varrho}\right)_2 - \left(\dfrac{\mu}{\varrho}\right)_1\right]} = 0·14 \text{ mm}.$

(b) By the factor $1/1·46$.

9.10. As, even when $\lambda > \lambda_K$, in the case of molybdenum τ/ϱ is considerably greater than $\dfrac{\varrho}{\varrho}\left(\dfrac{\varrho}{\varrho} \approx 0\cdot2\right)$, the magnitudes of the discontinuities in μ/ϱ and in τ/ϱ at the edge of the K-absorption band are practically equal. Hence

$$\frac{(\mu/\varrho)_{\lambda'}}{(\mu/\varrho)_{\lambda''}} \approx 7\cdot5.$$

9.11. From the table of Appendix 8 we find:

(a) for an iron foil $\lambda_K = 1\cdot74$ Å,

(b) for a copper foil $\lambda_K = 1\cdot377$ Å.

9.12. The phase velocity is $w = c/n$, where c is the velocity of light in vacuum and n the refraction index ($n = \sqrt{\varepsilon}$).

The group velocity is

$$g = w - \lambda \frac{\mathrm{d}w}{\mathrm{d}\lambda},$$

where $\lambda = w/\nu$. Hence, after simple transformation we find that $g = nc$. It should be noted that $w > c$ (from the condition that $n < 1$). However, this situation does not contradict the theory of relativity, which states that the velocity of signals (of the transfer of energy) cannot be greater than c. But it is well known that phase velocity does not describe the velocity of signals.

9.13. The distance in question is of the order of $0\cdot1$ mm. This can be overcome by diffracting the X-rays at glancing incidence to the grating (see 9.22).

9.14. $5\cdot07$ Å.

9.15. (a) $d = 2\cdot81$ Å, and for the grating constant $a = 2d = 5\cdot62$ Å.

9.16. We write down the Laue conditions for an interference maximum for a simple cubic lattice:

$$d(\cos\alpha - \cos\alpha_0) = k_1\lambda,$$
$$d(\cos\beta - \cos\beta_0) = k_2\lambda,$$
$$d(\cos\gamma - \cos\gamma_0) = k_3\lambda.$$

Here d is the lattice constant, λ the wavelength and k_1, k_2 and k_3 the orders of the spectra; the angles α_0, β_0, γ_0 and α, β, γ describe respectively the direction of the incoming wave and the directions along which the interference maxima appear.

We must also take into account the geometrical relation between the angles α, β and γ:

$$\cos^2 \alpha + \cos^2 \beta + \cos^2 \gamma = 1.$$

As can be easily shown, the solution of this system of four equations in the three unknowns α, β and γ is possible only for the following values of λ:

$$\lambda = -2d \frac{k_1 \cos \alpha_0 + k_2 \cos \beta_0 + k_3 \cos \gamma_0}{k_1^2 + k_2^2 + k_3^2}.$$

9.17. to 9.19. See Reference 1.

9.20. Beginning with lithium (K-series) and sodium (L-series).

9.21. Moseley's law proves the correctness of the order of the elements in the periodic table. The correction factor determines the magnitude of the screening of the nuclear charge by the electrons.

9.22. $1 \cdot 74 \times 10^8$ cm^{-1}; $0 \cdot 575$ Å; $21 \cdot 6$ keV.

9.23. $0 \cdot 9$; $0 \cdot 9$ and $0 \cdot 95$.

9.24. $0 \cdot 25$; 0; $-2 \cdot 0$.

9.25. $0 \cdot 9$; $1 \cdot 8$; $2 \cdot 4$; $3 \cdot 3$. The differences arise from the different screening of the nuclear charge, Z, in the L, M, N shells.

9.26. (a) $60 \cdot 5$; $62 \cdot 2$ and $84 \cdot 5$ kV.

(b) The wavelength of the absorption edge.

9.27. At first the continuous X spectrum will appear, its short-wave edge shifting toward the region of large frequencies. After that, the lines of the characteristic spectrum will slowly begin to be excited, the K-series being excited last. The total radiation power of the continuous and the characteristic spectrum will continue to grow, but the position of the lines of the characteristic spectrum will remain unchanged.

9.28. Yes.

9.29. $25 \cdot 5$ keV.

9.30. (a) 785.

(b) For the six-fold ionized nitrogen atom.

9.31. (a) $v = \sqrt{\dfrac{2hc}{m} \dfrac{\lambda_K - \lambda_\alpha}{\lambda_K \lambda_\alpha}} \approx 2 \cdot 7 \times 10^9 \text{ cm/sec},$

where c is the velocity of light, m the mass of the electron, λ_K and λ respectively the wavelengths of the excitation limit of the molybdenum K-series and of the K_α line of silver.

(b) $4 \cdot 4 \times 10^9 \text{ cm/sec}.$

9.32. Electrons of the given energy are knocked out of the K-shell of the atom

$$E_K = h c R (Z - 1)^2 - e U_3 = 260 \text{ eV},$$

where Z is the atomic number of aluminium.

9.33. $\lambda_L = \dfrac{\lambda_\alpha \lambda_K}{\lambda_\alpha - \lambda_K} = 172 \text{ Å}.$

9.34. Owing to spin orbit splitting, as in optical spectra (cf. Chapter 6).

9.35. $^2P_{3/2}$. This follows from the fact that the total momentum of the closed shell is equal zero; for this to be so it is necessary that the momentum (and the state) of the electron leaving the atom should be equal to the momentum of the new state of the atom. These momenta should differ only in direction.

9.36. $K \to L$ and $K \to M$ two spectral lines each, $L \to M$ seven.

9.37.   5475 eV (K),   514 eV (L) and   35 eV (M).

9.38. $A \approx h c \left[\dfrac{1}{\lambda} + \dfrac{3}{4} R (Z - 1)^2 \right] = 15 \text{ keV},$

where h is Planck's constant, c the velocity of light, R Rydberg's constant and Z the atomic number.

9.39. (a) $0 \cdot 1315$ Å $(K_{\alpha 2})$, $0 \cdot 1265$ Å $(K_{\alpha 1})$
(b) $115 \cdot 3$ keV (K), $21 \cdot 8$ keV (L).

10.1. $^2S_{1/2}$, $^2P_{1/2,\ 3/2}$, $^4P_{1/2,\ 3/2,\ 5/2}$, $^5D_{0,\ 1,\ 2,\ 3,\ 4}$.

10.2. 4; 7 and 7.

10.3. $(2S + 1)(2L + 1)$. In a strong magnetic field.

10.4. It gives the degeneracy of a state with the given L and S.

10.5. (a) 15 (phosphorus)
(b) 46 (palladium).

10.6. (a)   2,   (b) $2(2l + 1)$,   (c) $\sum\limits_{l=0}^{n-1} 2(2l + 1) = 2n^2$,

10.8. The "ideal" periodic system is based on two somewhat oversimplified assumptions:
(a) each electron in an atom is located in a central field;
(b) there is no mutual interaction between the electrons in the atom.

10.9. For potassium.

10.10. From Pauli's principle it follows that for electrons in closed subshells,

$$M_L = \sum m_l = 0 \quad \text{and} \quad M_S = \sum m_s = 0.$$

Since M_L and M_S represent the projections of L and S on an arbitrary z axis, it follows that the angular momenta P_L, P_S and also P_J vanish.

10.11. Applying the ordinary rules for the addition of l and s, we obtain (for light atoms Russell–Saunders coupling is known to be valid): $L = 3, 2, 1$; $S = 1, 0$.

Since, evidently, two values of S correspond to each term with given L we have 6 different terms altogether.

10.12. The electrons in the incomplete subshells have different quantum numbers and hence the requirement of the Pauli principle is already satisfied. Using the ordinary rules for the addition of l and s, we get:

$$L = 5, 4, 3, 2, 1; \quad S = 1, 0.$$

Combining these with each other we find the following types of term:

$$^{1,3}P, \quad ^{1,3}D, \quad ^{1,3}F, \quad ^{1,3}G \quad \text{and} \quad ^{1,3}H.$$

10.13. (b) $\qquad\qquad ^2S_{3/2}(N), \quad ^3P_2(O).$

10.14. (a) $^2D_{3/2}$,

(b) $^3F_2$.

10.15. From Hund's rule we find d^5, $S = 5/2$, $M_{L\max} = \sum m_l = 0$, and hence $L = 0$. Thus the fundamental term is $^6S_{5/2}$ (sextet).

10.16. Let us set up a table showing the arrangement of the electrons according to their quantum numbers, when the Pauli principle is taken into account (Table 1). Here we can omit the data for those electrons which give negative values for the sum of the projections of M_L and M_S; one can easily see that they do not give anything new.

TABLE 1

m_l	m_s						
$+1$	↑	↑	↑	↓	↑↓	↑↓	↑
0	↑	↑	↓	↑	—	↑	↑↓
-1	↑	↓	↑	↑	↑	—	—
M_L	0	0	0	0	1	2	1
M_S	3/2	1/2	1/2	1/2	1/2	1/2	1/2
Term	^4S					^2D	^2P

For reasons of clarity we denote the projection of the spin (m_s) of each electron by an arrow directed upwards $(m_s = 1/2)$ or downwards $(m_s = -1/2)$.

The presence of the states with $M_L = 2$ and $M_S = 1/2$ gives us the term ^2D to which two other states must correspond: $M_L = 1$, $M_s = 1/2$ and $M_L = 0$, $M_S = 1/2$. Of the remaining arrangements the state with $M_L = 1$, $M_S = 1/2$ gives the term ^2P, to which the state $M_L = 0$, $M_s = 1/2$ must also correspond. The last two states

$$M_L = 0, \; M_S = 3/2 \quad \text{and} \quad M_L = 0, \; M_S = 1/2$$

belong to the term ^4S. Consequently, for the given configuration three types of term are possible: ^2D, ^2P and ^4S.

According to the Hund rule the ground term is $^4S_{3/2}$.

TABLE 2

m_l	m_s			
	p^1		p^5	
+1	↑	−	↑↓	↑↓
0	−	↑	↑↓	↑
−1	−	−	↑	↑↓
M_L	1	0	1	0
M_S	1/2	1/2	1/2	1/2
Term	^2P		^2P	

10.17. See Table 2.

For an explanation of the table see the solution to problem 10.16.

10.18. The number of states with the same quantum numbers n and l is $N = 2(2l + 1)$. In distributing k electrons over these states one must take into account the limitation imposed by Pauli's principle: there must be no electrons with the same pairs of quantum numbers m_l and m_s. Consequently, the problem is reduced to finding the number of combinations of N elements k at a time:

$$C_N^k = \frac{N(N-1)(N-2)\cdots(N-k+1)}{k!}.$$

In our case $C_N^k = 120$.

10.19. According to Hund's rule $S = 3/2$, $L = 3$ and $J = L - S = 3/2$. After calculating the Landé factor g for the given term we have: $\mu = g\mu_0\sqrt{J(J+1)} = 0\cdot775$ Bohr magnetons.

10.20. Such configurations are respectively np^5, nd^4 and nf^9. are supplementary to the closed configurations np^6, nd^{10} and nd^{14} (whose quantum numbers L, S and J are zero), and hence they should have the same possible type of term as the configurations given in the problem.

10.21. Let us set up the table of possible arrangements of the electrons (Table 5), taking into account that the Pauli principle imposes limitations only on equivalent electrons, i.e. those that have the same values of n and l.

TABLE 5

m	m							
$+1$	↑	↑	↑	↑	↑	↑	↑↓	—
0	↑↑	↑↓	↑	↓	↓↑	↑	↑	↑↑↑
-1	—	—	↑	↑	—	↓	—	—
M_L	1	1	0	0	1	0	2	0
M_S	3/2	1/2	3/2	1/2	1/2	1/2	1/2	1/2
Term	^4P	^2P					^2D	^2S

Here the projections of the spins of the p-electrons are denoted by short arrows, and those of the s-electrons by longer arrows.

From the Table it is clear that the following values of L and S are possible: $L = 2, 1, 0$; $S = 3/2, 1/2$.

The possible types of term are: ^2D, ^4P, ^2P, ^2S.

The fundamental term $^4P_{1/2}$ is found by the Hund rule.

10.22. (a), (b), (c) and (d). These properties depend on the outer electrons of atoms.

11.1. Of the total number $3n$ of degrees of freedom of a n-atomic molecule three are translational, three or two (the latter for linear molecules) are rotational. These degrees of freedom describe the motion of the molecule as a whole. The remaining $3n-6$ or $3n-5$ (for linear molecules) degrees of freedom describe the vibrations of the molecules.

(a) 4 and 7.

(b) 3, 9 and 15.

11.2. In the general case

$$\overline{E} = \frac{3}{2} kT + i_{\text{rot}} \frac{kT}{2} + i_{\text{vib}} kT,$$

where i_{rot} and i_{vib} are the numbers of rotational and vibrational degrees of freedom of the molecule. Hence

$$\overline{E}(\text{PCl}_3) = 9kT, \quad \overline{E}(\text{C}_2\text{H}_2) = 9.5kT.$$

11.3. From the relations $p = n_0 kT$ and

$$E = n_0 \left(\frac{3}{2} kT + i_{\text{rot}} \frac{kT}{2} + i_{\text{vib}} kT \right),$$

where n_0 is the number of molecules in 1 cm^3, and i_{rot} and i_{vib} are the numbers of rotational and vibrational degrees of freedom, we have $p = \dfrac{E}{3n-3}$ and $p = \dfrac{E}{3n-2.5}$ (for linear molecules).

11.4. $\omega = \dfrac{\hbar \sqrt{r(r+1)}}{\mu d^2}$, where μ is the reduced mass of the molecule. 1.565×10^{11} rad/sec (S_2) and 3.51×10^{12} rad/sec (HJ).

11.5. $T = \dfrac{2\hbar^2}{3k\mu d^2}$, where k is Boltzmann's constant and μ the reduced mass of the molecule. We find respectively: 117, 2.76, and 0.458°K.

11.6. $E = 2hB$, where B is the constant of rotation.

(a) $2\cdot66 \times 10^{-4}$ eV,
(b) $1\cdot02 \times 10^{-4}$ eV,
(c) $2\cdot94 \times 10^{-4}$ eV.

11.7. The degree of degeneracy is $2R + 1$. It is equal to the number of the possible projections of the angular momentum on an arbitrary z axis ($P_z = m_R \hbar$, where the quantum number $m_R = R, R - 1, ..., -R$).

11.8. First of all, let us estimate the minimum rotational energy of the molecule about the figure axis. Let us assume for simplicity that the molecule consists of identical nuclei. This assumption will clearly have no effect on the final result. Then

$$E_{r\,min} = \frac{3\cdot3 \times 10^{49}\, \hbar^2}{A^{5/2}}.$$

Hence it follows that even in the most unfavourable case ($A \approx 200$) $E_{r\,min}$ will be of the order of several thousand electron volts, which corresponds to a temperature of $\sim 40 \times 10^6\,°K$! This is why at ordinary temperatures this degree of freedom a molecule is in a "frozen" state.

11.9. Apart from a term mc^2 that accounts for the rest and translational energies of the molecule its total energy is

$$E = E_e + h\,\nu\left(v + \frac{1}{2}\right) + h\,BR(R + 1),$$

where E_e is the excitation energy of the electronic levels of the molecule.

11.10. $$\frac{E_{v1}}{E_{r1}} = \frac{4\pi^2\,\nu\,\mu\,d^2}{h},$$

where ν is the vibrational eigenfrequency of the molecule, μ its reduced mass and d the distance between the nuclei. This ratio is respectively $35\cdot8$, 175 and 287.

11.11. Up to the level with the rotational quantum number $r \approx 48$.

11.12. $E = D - h\nu v$, where D is the dissociation energy, measured from the "zero" vibrational level of the molecule, and v

is the vibrational quantum number. We have 3·388 and 3·689 eV, respectively.

11.13. From the condition $\dfrac{d}{dv} E_v = 0$ we find the maximum value of the vibrational quantum number $v_{max} = \dfrac{1-x}{2x}$. Then

$$E_{v\,max} = \frac{h\,c\,\bar{v}}{4x} = 2\text{·}47\ \text{eV}.$$

11.14. Let us start from the expression $E_{max} - E_0 = E_{dis} + E$, where E_{max} and E_0 are the maximum and the zero vibrational energies. Expressing E_{max} as a function of the anharmonic parameter x, we find

$$x = \frac{h\,c\,\bar{v}}{4(E_{dis} + E + E_0)} = 3\text{·}59 \times 10^{-3}.$$

11.15. $N_1/N_2 = 3\text{·}12$.

11.16. $\dfrac{N_{rot}}{N_{vib}} = 23\text{·}1$. In carrying out the calculations the degeneracy of the rotational energy level must be taken into account.

11.17. By the definition of an average

$$\bar{E} = \frac{\displaystyle\sum_{v=0}^{\infty} E_v\, e^{-E_v/kT}}{\displaystyle\sum_{v=0}^{\infty} e^{-E_v/kT}}$$

where the summation is over all possible values of energy E_v.

To find the required value we note first of all that the above expression can be represented as follows:

$$\bar{E} = \theta^2 \frac{\partial}{\partial \theta} \ln\left(\sum_{v=0}^{\infty} e^{-E_v/\theta}\right),$$

where $\theta = kT$.

It can be easily seen that we have under the logarithm sign the sum of an infinite geometric progression:

$$\sum_{v=0}^{\infty} e^{-E_v/\theta} = \sum_{v=0}^{\infty} e^{-h\,v\,(v+1/2)/\theta} = \frac{e^{-h\,v/2\theta}}{1 - e^{-h\,v/\theta}}.$$

Taking the derivative $\partial/\partial\theta$ of the logarithm of this last expression, we finally obtain, after simplification

$$\bar{E} = \frac{h\,\nu}{2} + \frac{h\,\nu}{e^{h\,\nu/k\,T} - 1}\,.$$

	T° K	$\bar{E}_{qu}$, eV	$\bar{E}_{cl}$, eV
11.18.	300	$3\cdot86 \times 10^{-10}$	$0\cdot026$
	3000	$7\cdot54 \times 10^{-2}$	$0\cdot26$

11.19. (a)
$$C_{V\,\text{vib}} = \frac{\partial E_v}{\partial T} = \frac{R\left(\dfrac{h\,\nu}{k\,T}\right)^2 e^{h\,\nu/k\,T}}{(e^{h\,\nu/k\,T} - 1)^2}\,,$$

where R is the universal gas constant and k Boltzmann's constant.

(b) $\sim 740^\circ$K.

11.20. $\dfrac{3}{2}R$, $\dfrac{5}{2}R$ and $\dfrac{7}{2}R$.

11.21. See, for instance, Reference 1.

11.22. (a)
$$\Delta E_R = \frac{\hbar^2}{I}\,R,$$

where $R = 0, 1, 2, \dots$ is the rotational quantum number of the top levels.

(b)
$$\Delta\,\bar{\nu} = \frac{h}{2\pi\,c\,I} = \text{const}.$$

Here I is the moment of inertia of the molecule.

11.23. (b) Decreases by $1\cdot035\,\hbar$.

11.24. (a) $2\cdot72 \times 10^{-40}$ g cm^2;

(b) $1\cdot29$ Å;

(c) $5\cdot47 \times 10^{12}$ sec^{-1}.

11.26.
$$\frac{\Delta\,\nu}{\nu} = -\frac{\Delta\,\mu}{\mu} = -0\cdot0015,$$

where μ is the reduced mass of the molecule.

11.27. The relative isotopic shift for a mixture of carbon molecules is approximately 40 times smaller.

11.28. The dissociation energy of the H_2^+ molecule is larger by

$$\Delta E = \frac{h\,c\,\nu}{2}\left(1 - \frac{1}{\sqrt{2}}\right) = 0{\cdot}08 \text{ eV}.$$

11.29. Two σ-electrons and four π- and δ-electrons each.

11.30. (a) The parity is odd for the first two molecules, since they have an even number of electrons ($S = 0, 1, 2, \ldots$). It is even for the others.

(b) $^1\Sigma_0,\ ^3\Sigma_1,\ ^2\Pi_{1/2,\ 3/2}.$

11.31. Three.

11.32. $7{\cdot}49 \times 10^{14}$ and $7{\cdot}51 \times 10^{14} \text{ sec}^{-1}$.

11.33. It increases by one.

11.34. $m = \dfrac{m_0\,k}{4\pi^2\,m_0\,c^2(\Delta\,\bar{\nu})^2 - k} \approx 20 \times 10^{-24}\,\text{g},$

which corresponds to the mass of a carbon atom. Here m_0 is the mass of an oxygen atom.

11.35. $1{\cdot}24 \times 10^{14} \text{ sec}^{-1}$; $9{\cdot}7 \times 10^5 \text{ d/cm}$.

11.36. $\Delta T = \left(\dfrac{1}{T} - \dfrac{k \ln \eta}{h\,\bar{\nu}\,c}\right)^{-1} - T \times 100°\text{K},$

where k is Boltzmann's constant and $\bar{\nu}$ the wave number of the vibrations of a chlorine molecule.

11.37. The deviation from Stokes' law shown by the presence in the fluorescent spectrum of shorter wavelengths than those of the exciting spectrum, is due to inelastic collisions of the original quanta with excited molecules.

11.38. The maser is a device by which very monochromatic electromagnetic radiation which is very stable in frequency may be obtained. (MASER stands for Microwave Amplification by Stimulated Emission of Radiation). The essential feature of a Maser is the use of the principle of stimulated emission to cause atomic or molecular transitions to take place in phase with one another. One form of maser utilizes vibrational transitions of ammonia molecules by allowing a beam of molecules to pass through an inhomogeneous magnetic field. Molecules in a given vibrational state may be selected by allowing them to pass through an aperture into a resonant cavity tuned to the frequency of the molecular transition. The molecules then emit their vibrational energy into the cavity synchronously in the form of microwave radiation.

12.1. $\quad \tau = \dfrac{1}{N_0} \displaystyle\int\limits_0^\infty t\lambda\, N\, \mathrm{d}t = \dfrac{1}{\lambda}, \quad \text{where} \quad N = N_0 e^{-\lambda t}.$

12.2. $6\cdot5 \times 10^9$ years, 2300 years and $5\cdot52$ days; and the half lives $4\cdot5 \times 10^9$ years, 1590 years and $3\cdot8$ days respectively.

12.3. $\qquad m = M_\mathrm{U}\, \dfrac{\mu_\mathrm{Pb}}{\mu_\mathrm{U}} \left(1 - e^{-\ln 2\frac{t}{T}}\right) = 275\,\mathrm{g},$

where M_U is the initial mass of the uranium isotope, μ_Pb and μ_U are the masses of gram atoms of lead and uranium.

12.4. (a) $4\cdot5 \times 10^9$ years
(b) $1\cdot87 \times 10^9$ years.

12.5. $3\cdot7 \times 10^{10}\ \mathrm{sec}^{-1}$.

12.6. $6\cdot62 \times 10^4\ \mathrm{sec}^{-1} = 1\cdot79\ \mu\mathrm{C}$ (microcurie).

12.7. See Reference 1.

12.8. $\qquad v = \dfrac{N_0}{N} e^{-\ln 2\frac{t}{T}} \approx 6\ \text{litres}.$

12.9. The total kinetic energy liberated in the disintegration of each such nucleus is equal to the sum of the kinetic energies of the alpha particle and of the residual nucleus. Taking into account also the law of conservation of momentum, we finally have:

$$E = E_\alpha \left(1 + \frac{m}{M}\right) = 8\cdot5\ \mathrm{MeV},$$

where E_α is the kinetic energy of the alpha particle, m its mass and M the mass of the residual nucleus.

12.10. $Q = \dfrac{N \varrho\, E}{\mu} \left(1 + \dfrac{m}{M}\right)\left(1 - e^{-\ln 2\frac{t}{T}}\right) = 275\ \mathrm{kcal},$

where N is Avogadro's number, μ the mass of a gram-atom of plutonium, m the mass of the alpha particle and M the mass of the residual nucleus.

12.11. Po^{216}.

12.12. From the table of Appendix 9 we find: 5 alpha decays and consequently 5 C.

12.13. Let us set up the differential equation for the rate of accumulation of the radioactive element B:

$$\frac{d}{dt} N_B = -\lambda_B N_B + \lambda_A N_A,$$

or

$$\frac{d}{dt} N_B + \lambda_B N_B = \lambda_A N_A(0) e^{-\lambda_A t}.$$

The solution of this equation, taking into account that $N_B(0) = 0$, is:

$$N_B(t) = N_A(0) (c_1 e^{-\lambda_A t} + c_2 e^{-\lambda_B t}).$$

The values of the constants c_1 and c_2 are obtained by substituting the last expression into the differential equation. We finally have:

$$N_B(t) = N_A(0) \frac{\lambda_A}{\lambda_B - \lambda_A} (e^{-\lambda_A t} - e^{-\lambda_B t}).$$

12.14. From the solution of the preceding problem it follows that, since $\lambda_B > \lambda_A$ for an interval of time considerably larger than the mean life time of the nuclei A, we can write

$$N_B(t) = \frac{\lambda_A}{\lambda_B - \lambda_A} N_A(0) e^{-\lambda_A t}.$$

Hence it is evident that the numbers of nuclei A and B will decrease at the same rate (the exponents are equal).

Consequently

$$\frac{N_B}{N_A} = \frac{\lambda_A}{\lambda_B - \lambda_A}.$$

Such a state is called a state of transient radioactive equilibrium.

12.15. (a) The instant when the two isotopes come into equilibrium is found from the condition:

$$\frac{d}{dt} N_B = 0.$$

Differentiating N_B with respect to time (see the expression for N_B in the solution of problem 12.13) and equating the result so obtained to zero, we find:

$$t = \frac{T_A T_B \ln \dfrac{T_B}{T_A}}{(T_B - T_A) \ln 2} = 10\cdot7 \text{ min}.$$

12.16. $\qquad t = -\dfrac{T}{\ln 2} \ln \left(1 - \dfrac{n\,\varrho}{q}\right) = 2\cdot9 \text{ years}.$

12.17. $0\cdot511$ and 931 MeV.

12.18. This is correct to with in the binding energy of electrons in an atom, which is usually negligible.

12.19. (a) $\qquad \Delta m = Z(m_{\mathrm{H}} - m_n) + A(m_n - 1) - \Delta,$

where Δm is the mass defect and Δ is the mass decrement, Z and A are the numbers of protons and nucleons in the nucleus respectively and m_{H} and m_n are the masses of the hydrogen atom and of the neutron in MU.

(b) He^4 ($0\cdot00387$ and $0\cdot03037$ MU), C^{12} ($0\cdot00380$ and $0\cdot09892$ MU), $\mathrm{0}^{16}$ (0 and $0\cdot13696$ MU).

12.20. H^2 ($0\cdot00238$ MU; $2\cdot215$ MeV), H^3 ($0\cdot00910$ MU; $8\cdot47$ MeV), He^4 ($0\cdot03037$ MU; $28\cdot2$ MeV), Be^9 ($0\cdot06242$ MU; $58\cdot1$ MeV).

12.21. H^3 ($0\cdot00910$ MU; $8\cdot47$ MeV), He^3 ($0\cdot00822$ MU; $7\cdot65$ MeV). The binding energy of He^3 is smaller, on account of the electrostatic repulsion of the protons in its nucleus.

12.22. $14\cdot4$ MeV.

12.23. $19\cdot8$ MeV (proton), $20\cdot55$ MeV (neutron). The binding energy of a proton is smaller than the binding energy of a neutron on account of the electrostatic repulsion.

12.24. $6\cdot02085$ MU.

12.25. (a) $\qquad Q = M(A, Z) - M(A, Z - 1) - 2m,$

where M is the mass of the atom and m the rest mass of the electron.

(b) $0\cdot96$ MeV.

12.26. From the laws of conservation of energy and momentum

$$p_\beta = p_B,$$
$$Q = E_\beta + E_B,$$

where the index β refers to the positron and B to the boron nucleus. We express E_B by means of Q, using the relativistic relation between the energy and the momentum of a positron:

$$p^2 c^2 = E_\beta (E_\beta + 2m_0 c^2).$$

Thus we have

$$E_\beta \approx \frac{Q(Q + 2m_0 c^2)}{2M c^2} = 93 \text{ eV}.$$

12.27. $Q = 8E_{\text{He}} - 7E_{\text{Li}} = 17 \cdot 3 \text{ MeV},$

where E_{He} and E_{Li} are the binding energies per nucleon of the corresponding nuclei.

12.28. 5·95 MeV.

12.29. (a) 7·16 MeV, (b) 4·04 MeV, (c) 4·01 MeV.

12.30. 3·38 and 1·82 MeV. The difference arises from the fact that the binding energy of the Be^7 nucleus is greater than the sum of the binding energies of He^3 and He^4.

12.31. Neglecting the energy of the neutrons we find from the laws of conservation of energy and momentum that

$$v_\alpha = \sqrt{\frac{2M Q}{m(m + M)}} = 9 \cdot 26 \times 10^8 \text{ cm/sec},$$

$$v_{\text{Li}} = \sqrt{\frac{2m Q}{M(m + M)}} = 5 \cdot 27 \times 10^8 \text{ cm/sec},$$

where Q is the reaction energy and M and m the masses of the Li^7 and He^4 nuclei respectively.

12.32. (b) $T = \frac{2}{3} \frac{e^2}{k \, r} \sim 2 \times 10^9 \,^\circ\text{K},$

where k is Boltzmann's constant and r the distance corresponding to the maximum potential energy of the Coulomb interaction. The fusion reaction can take place at a lower temperature ($\sim 10^7 \,^\circ\text{K}$) for two reasons: (1) at this temperature there are deuterons of energies considerably greater than the average energy (in the tail of Maxwell's distribution) and (2) on account of the quantum tunnel effect.

12.33. (a) 7·25 MeV, (b) 1·56 MeV.

12.34. From the laws of conservation of energy and momentum we find

$$E_\gamma - E = 2E_p,$$

where E is the binding energy of the deuteron (we neglect the difference of the proton and the neutron masses). Calculating the kinetic energy E_p from the data of the problem we have

$$E = E_\gamma - \frac{e^2 \varrho^2 H^2}{m c^2} = 2 \cdot 23 \,\text{MeV}.$$

where m is the mass of the proton.

12.35. When the kinetic energy of the incoming particles is equal to the threshold value, the relative velocity of the particles resulting from the reaction is zero, i.e. $v_{m'} = v_{M'}$. In this case the conservation laws of energy and momentum can be written in the form:

$$E_{\text{thr}} = E_{m'} + E_{M'} + |Q|,$$
$$p_m = p_{m'} + p_{M'},$$

where

$$\frac{p_{m'}}{p_{M'}} = \frac{M'}{m'}.$$

We obtain the expression for E_{thr} by solving this system of three equations.

12.36. (a) $0 \cdot 235$ MeV.

(b) From the laws of conservation of energy and momentum we have, when the kinetic energy of the protons is equal to the threshold energy

$$v = \frac{\sqrt{2m\,E_{\text{thr}}}}{M + m} = 2 \cdot 39 \times 10^8 \,\text{cm/sec},$$

where m and M are the masses of the proton and the Li⁷ nucleus respectively.

12.37. From the conservation laws of energy and momentum

$$Q = E_{\text{p}}\left(1 + \frac{A_p}{A_0}\right) - E_{\text{d}}\left(1 - \frac{A_d}{A_0}\right) = 4 \cdot 04 \,\text{MeV},$$

where A_{p}, A_α and A_0 are the mass numbers of the proton, deuteron, and the recoil nucleus (H³) respectively. The reaction is exothermic: $Q > 0$.

12.38. $E_n = \dfrac{M_C}{M_C + m_n}\left(Q + \dfrac{M_C - m_\alpha}{M_C} E\right) = 8.52$ MeV,

where M_C is the mass of the carbon nucleus, m_α the mass of the alpha particle and m_n the mass of the neutron.

12.39. (a) $\qquad R = a\left(\dfrac{E_p + Q^{3/2}}{m_\alpha}\right) = 10.4$ cm,

where

$$a = 9.8 \times 10^{-28} \text{ sec}^3/\text{cm}^2$$

E_p is the kinetic energy of the protons, Q the reaction energy and m the mass of the alpha particle.

(b) 165° 20′.

12.40. $\qquad \dfrac{n_\alpha}{n_f} = \ln 2 \dfrac{\tau_f}{T_\alpha} \sim 2.5 \times 10^9,$

where τ_f is the mean life for spontaneous fission and T_α the half-life period.

12.41. Yes, since the excitation energy of the U^{236} nucleus formed in this case is 6.42 MeV. This can easily be found from the mass defect of the reaction.

12.42. About 1 MeV.

12.43. $\quad E_f = 234 \times 8.6 - 236 \times 7.8 = 170$ MeV.

12.44. The mean free path of neutrons in the material is $\lambda \cong 1/N\sigma$ where N is the number of atoms/cm³. [3]

For uranium, density 18.7 g/cm³, $\lambda \cong 0.035$ cm. Hence practically all the incident flux will be absorbed in 1 cm of material. Energy release $= 10^{10} \times 200$ MeV/sec $= 0.32$ W.

12.45. See Reference 4.

12.46. $\qquad \eta = \dfrac{4m M}{(m + M)^2} 100\%,$

where m and M are the masses of the neutron and of the nucleus with which it collides inelastically.

(a) 89 per cent,

(b) 36 per cent,

(c) 28.4 per cent, and

(d) 1.67 per cent.

12.47. (a) When a neutron is scattered through an angle ϑ in the laboratory system of coordinates its kinetic energy is

$$E(\vartheta) = E_0 \cos^2 \vartheta.$$

This can be easily seen from the momentum vector diagram (Fig. 58). Here p_0 and p_0' are the momenta of the neutron before

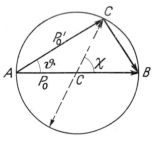

FIG. 58

and after it is scattered by an angle ϑ. Since in the centre of mass system the scattering is spherically symmetric, the element of solid angle is

$$d\omega = 2\pi \sin \chi \, d\chi.$$

Passing to the laboratory system, one must take into account that $\chi = 2\vartheta$, and therefore

$$d\omega = 4\pi \sin 2\vartheta \, d\vartheta.$$

Hence we find the average value of the kinetic energy of the neutron after scattering:

$$\bar{E} = \frac{1}{4\pi} \int\limits_0^{\pi/2} E(\vartheta) \, d\omega = \frac{1}{2} E_0.$$

(b) $\vartheta = 45°$.

12.48.
$$n = \frac{\log \dfrac{3kT}{2E_0}}{\log \cos^2 \vartheta} = 27 \cdot 5.$$

12.49. About 8 per cent (this energy is produced by gamma radiation and neutrons alone).

12.50. The multiplication factor is the average number of subsequent fissions caused by the neutrons which arise as the result of the fission of one nucleus. The power of the reactor decreases, remains constant, and increases respectively.

12.51. During the life-time of n generations of neutrons the number of fissions (the power of the reactor) increases by a factor of kn. Hence

$$t = \tau n = \tau \frac{\log \eta}{\log k} = 24 \text{ sec}.$$

12.52. $$m = \frac{\mu M J}{E N} = 1 \cdot 53 \text{ kg}$$

where μ is the mass of a gram-atom of U^{235}, M the mass of the TNT equivalent, J its thermal equivalent and N the Avogadro number.

12.53. 172 g, 120 tons.

12.54. (a) $Q = 1 \cdot 94 \times 10^{10}$ cal, $2 \cdot 77 \times 10^3$ tons coal.

(b) $$Q = \frac{1}{4} N E = 1 \cdot 38 \times 10^{11} \text{ cal}, \ 1 \cdot 96 \times 10^4 \text{ t of coal}.$$

Here N is Avogadro's number and E the energy of each reaction.

12.55. 56 kg.
(a) $1 \cdot 7 \times 10^8$ t;
(b) $62 \cdot 1$ t;
(c) $8 \cdot 7$ t.

13.1. Isotopes: O^{14} and O^{16}. Isobars: C^{14}, N^{14} and O^{14}. Isotopes B^{12} and N^{14}. Mirror nuclei: C^{14} and O^{14}.

13.2. $\sim 10^{14}$ g/cm^3.

13.3. Nuclear radii are determined from experiments on scattering of protons and alpha particles, the scattering cross-sections of fast neutrons ($\lambda \ll R$); the alpha decay theory, the diffraction of high energy electrons ($\lambda \sim R$), the binding energy differences of mirror nuclei, the analysis of gamma spectra of mesic atoms and by means of other methods; probably the most important modern method is that of electron diffraction.

13.4. For this to happen the wavelength of the electron should be of the order of magnitude of the dimensions of the nucleus ($\lambda \approx R$). The energy of such electrons, as is easily seen, is $E \approx hc/R$. Hence we find: ~ 500 MeV for He^4 and ~ 130 MeV for U.

13.5.
$$R = \frac{1 \cdot 2\, Z\, e^2}{(\Delta M + m_n - m_H)\, c^2},$$

where Z is the atomic number of the mirror nucleus with the smaller number of protons. Hence we have 3·11, 3·43, and 3·45 fermi respectively.

13.6. See Reference 2.

13.7. 36·9752 and 39·9744 MU.

13.8. From the condition $d\mu/dz = 0$ we have

$$Z = \frac{A}{1 \cdot 98 + 0.015\, A^{2/3}}.$$

Rounding off to the nearest integer we find that

Na_{11}^{23} (10·95), V_{23}^{51} (23·3), Y_{39}^{89} (39·1) and In_{49}^{114} (48·95).

13.9. 4·2 MeV.

13.10. (a) $\quad n \to p + e^- + \bar{\nu}, \quad p \to n + e^+ + \nu,$

where ν and $\bar{\nu}$ are the neutrino and the antineutrino, respectively.

(b) In the nuclei A' there will be an excess of neutrons. Consequently one of these will transform into a proton emitting a β-particle. In the nuclei A'', however, there is an excess of protons, and hence a β^+-particle is emitted.

13.11. From the condition

$$\Delta E = M(A, Z) - 2M(A/2, Z/2) > 0$$

we find that

$$\frac{Z^2}{A} \geqq 15\cdot7.$$

Putting $A \approx 2Z$, we get $Z \approx 31$.

13.12. (a) $Z^2/A \approx 45$.

(b) For

$$U^{238}\frac{Z^2}{A} = 35\cdot5.$$

The fission of such nuclei is explained by the tunnel effect.

13.13. The independence of nuclear forces of the electric charge of the nucleon. Figure 59 (a) corresponds to the n–n and n–p interactions, while 59 (b) corresponds to the p–p interaction.

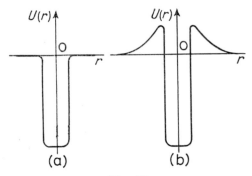

FIG. 59

13.14. (a) We start from the Schrödinger equation written in spherical polar coordinates:

$$\frac{1}{r^2}\frac{\mathrm{d}}{\mathrm{d}r}\left(r^2\frac{\mathrm{d}\psi}{\mathrm{d}r}\right) + \frac{2\mu}{\hbar^2}(U_0 - E)\,\psi = 0,$$

where μ is the reduced mass of the deuteron ($m/2$, m is the nucleon mass). U_0 and E are here taken as absolute values.

Using the substitution $u(r) = r\psi$, we have

$(r < R)$ $\quad u_1'' + k_1^2 u_1 = 0$, $\quad$ where $\quad k_1 = \sqrt{m(U_0 - E)}/\hbar$,

$(r > R)$ $\quad u_2'' - k_2^2 u_2 = 0$, $\quad$ where $\quad k_2 = \sqrt{m E}/\hbar$.

Taking into account the condition the function ψ, must be finite we finally have

$$u_1 = A \sin k_1 r, \quad \psi_1 = A \frac{\sin k_1 r}{r},$$

$$u_2 = B\,e^{-k_2 r}, \quad \psi_2 = B \frac{e^{-k_2 r}}{r}.$$

Here A and B are constants determined from the condition that the wave function should be continuous at $r = R$ and from the normalization condition.

(b) From the requirement that ψ_1 and ψ_2 (or u_1 and u_2) should be continuous at the point $r = R$ it follows that

$$\tan k_1 R = -\frac{k_1}{k_2},$$

or

$$\tan \beta = -\frac{\hbar}{R \sqrt{m E}} \beta,$$

where

$$\beta = R \sqrt{m(U_0 - E)}/\hbar.$$

Solving this equation graphically (Fig. 60) we find $\beta \approx 1\cdot9$. Hence we can easily find U_0:

$$U_0 = E + \frac{1\cdot9^2\,\hbar^2}{m\,R^2} \approx 21 \text{ MeV}.$$

13.15. (a) The probability of finding the nucleons at a distance between r and $r + \mathrm{d}r$ apart is

$$W(r)\,\mathrm{d}r = \psi^2\,4\pi\,r^2\,\mathrm{d}r.$$

Into the given expression we substitute the functions ψ_1 and ψ_2, as obtained from the solution of the preceding problem; we get:

$$W_1(r)\,\mathrm{d}r = 4\pi\,A^2 \sin^2 k_1 r\,\mathrm{d}r \quad (r < R),$$

$$W_2(r)\,\mathrm{d}r = 4\pi\,B^2\,e^{-2k_2 r}\,\mathrm{d}r \quad (r > R).$$

The most probable distance between the nucleons corresponds to the maximum of the function $W_1(r)$ (it can be easily seen, that the derivative dW_2/dr of $W_2(r)$ is nowhere zero). From the condition that $dW_1/dr = 0$ we find that

$$r_{prob} = \frac{\pi\hbar}{2\sqrt{m(U_0 - E)}} = 2.33 \text{ fermi.}$$

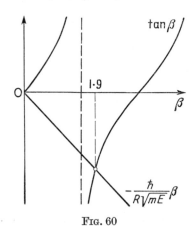

FIG. 60

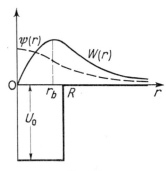

FIG. 61

(b) See Fig. 61.

13.16. All nuclei with half integer spin or, in other words, with odd mass number A: H^3, He^3, Li^7, Be^9 etc.

13.17. The fine structure is due to the spin of the electrons and the hyperfine structure to the spin of the nucleus.

13.18. (a) For the atoms with $I \leq J$ (J is the quantum number of the total angular momentum of the orbital electrons). In this case the number of the components is $2I + 1$.

(b) 2, 2, 1, 3, 2, 4.

13.19. $I = 7/2$. One can easily prove that $I < J$.

13.20. $$(2J + 1)(2I + 1) = 12 \text{ or } 24.$$

The ratio $1 : 2$ does not depend on I.

13.21. The intensity ratio of the spectral line components that arise as the result of a transition from the unsplit to the split level is equal to the ratio of their statistical weights. Therefore

$$0 \cdot 6 = \frac{2 F_1 + 1}{2 F_2 + 1} = \frac{I}{I + 1}.$$

Hence $I = 3/2$.

13.22. Since $J = 0$ we have in this case $F = I$. Therefore, the number of components is equal to $2I + 1$. Hence

$$I(\text{Be}^9) = 3/2, \ I(\text{C}^{13}) = 1/2.$$

13.23. In the field H_1 the coupling $J–I$ is broken. Here the nuclear spin I has no noticeable effect on the splitting of the beam: its magnetic moment is $\sim 1/2000 \, \mu_{\text{el}}$. As a result there are $2J + 1 = 2$ beams. In the field H_2, however, I and J are not decoupled J, so that each beam is split into another $2I + 1$ components. From the condition of the problem $2(2J + 1) = 8$, whence $I = 3/2$.

13.24. For resonance the frequency of the variable field f should be equal to ν, the Larmor precession frequency of the neutron

$$\left(\nu = g \, \frac{e \, H}{4\pi \, m_n \, c} \right), \text{ where } g = \frac{\mu_H}{\mu_n \, I},$$

I is the neutron spin. Hence

$$\mu_H = \frac{f h I}{H} = 1 \cdot 91 \, \mu_n, \quad \mu = 3 \cdot 32 \, \mu_n.$$

13.25. In the $^1S_0$ state the magnetic moment of the atom consists only of the magnetic moment of the nucleus. From the resonance condition we find the gyromagnetic ratio g of the nucleus:

$$g = \frac{f h}{\mu_n H} = 0 \cdot 34.$$

Hence we determine the spin of the nucleus

$$I = \frac{\mu_H}{g\,\mu_n} = 5/2\,.$$

13.26. From Fig. 62 it is evident that, since $g_s \neq g_l$ $\boldsymbol{\mu}$ does not coincide in direction with $\boldsymbol{j}$. As the result the vector $\boldsymbol{\mu}$ precesses about vector $\boldsymbol{j}$. This results in a magnetic moment averaged over

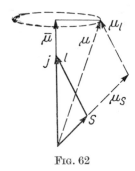

FIG. 62

time $\boldsymbol{\mu}$ which has the same direction as the vector $\boldsymbol{j}$. Just as in the vector model of the atom, here also:

$$\bar{\mu} = g_j\,\sqrt{j(j+1)}$$

nuclear magnetons.

13.27. From the vector model of the nucleons in the nucleus it follows that the averaged magnetic moment $\boldsymbol{\mu}$ (which coincides in direction with the vector J) is

$$\bar{\mu} = \mu_s \cos(\mathbf{s}\,\mathbf{j}) + \mu_l \cos(\mathbf{l}\,\mathbf{j})\,.$$

We have

$$\mu_s = g_s\,\sqrt{s(s+1)} \quad \text{and} \quad \mu_l = g_l\,\sqrt{l(l+1)}\,.$$

The cosines can be determined from the corresponding triangles by means of the cosine theorem, as follows

$$s^2 = j^2 + l^2 - 2\,|\,\mathbf{j}\,\mathbf{l}\,|\cos(\mathbf{l}\,\mathbf{j})\,,$$
$$l^2 = j^2 + s^2 - 2\,|\,\mathbf{j}\,\mathbf{s}\,|\cos(\mathbf{s}\,\mathbf{j})\,.$$

Substituting into the above expression for μ we get

$$\bar{\mu} = g_j\,\sqrt{j(j+1)}\,,$$

where

$$g_j = \frac{g_s + g_l}{2} + \frac{(g_s - g_l)\,[s(s+1) - l(l+1)]}{2_j\,(j+1)}.$$

13.28. For the proton we find (in nuclear magnetons):

$$\mu_p = \left(1 - \frac{2 \cdot 29}{j+1}\right)j, \quad \text{where} \quad j = l - 1/2,$$

$$\mu_p = \left(1 + \frac{2 \cdot 29}{j}\right)j, \quad \text{where} \quad j = l + 1/2,$$

and for the neutron

$$\mu_n = \frac{1 \cdot 91}{j+1}\,j, \quad \text{where} \quad j = l - 1/2,$$

$$\mu_n = -1 \cdot 91, \quad \text{for} \quad j = l + 1/2.$$

Consequently we have

	$s_{1/2}$	$p_{1/2}$	$p_{3/2}$
μ_p	2·79	−0·26	3·79
μ_n	−1·91	0·64	−1·91

13.29. $\mu_\alpha = 0 \cdot 88$ nuclear magnetons. The experimental value is 0·86.

13.30. If the electron existed as an independent particle inside the nucleus, the uncertainty of its momentum would be

$$\Delta p \sim \frac{\hbar}{10^{-12}} \sim 10^{-15}\ \text{g} \cdot \text{cm/sec}.$$

Such a value of the momentum corresponds, as can easily be shown, to a relativistic electron with an uncertainty in the kinetic energy of

$$\Delta E_k \sim \Delta p\, c \approx 20\ \text{MeV}.$$

However, the potential barrier of the nucleus for the electron is

$$U = \frac{Z\,e^2}{r} \sim 1 \cdot 4\ \text{MeV}.$$

Hence it is evident that the nucleus cannot contain the electron within its volume.

14.1. $E_p = \dfrac{4\,m_k\,m_p}{(m_k + m_p)^2}\,E\cos^2\varphi = 43{\cdot}7 \ keV, \quad E_k = 56{\cdot}3 \ keV.$

14.2. $\qquad m = \dfrac{M\,e^2\,\varrho^2\,H^2}{2M\,c^2\,E - e^2\,\varrho^2\,H^2} = 208$

electron masses, where M is the proton mass (μ-meson).

14.3. Let us consider the collision of the particles in the centre of mass system. In this case (one particle at rest), the velocity of the system is

$$V = \frac{m_1\,v}{m_1 + m_2}$$

and the velocity of the particles relative to it is

$$v_1 = v - V; \quad v_2 = -V.$$

The total kinetic energy of the two particles in the centre of mass system is:

$$E = \frac{m_1\,m_2}{m_1 + m_2}\cdot\frac{v^2}{2}.$$

The first factor here represents μ, the reduced mass of the particles. At the instant of closest approach the kinetic energy should be equal to the potential energy of their interaction, as given by the expression in the text of the problem.

14.4. See the solution of problem 3.5.

$$r_{\min} = \frac{e^2}{m\,v^2}\left(1 + \sqrt{1 + \cot^2\frac{\vartheta}{2}}\right) = 1{\cdot}18 \times 10^{-11}\,cm,$$

where m is the mass of the meson.

14.5. (a) The problem of the collision of the particles can be solved most easily by means of a vector diagram. It is set up in the following way. In the centre of mass system the momenta of the two particles are:

$$p_M = p_m = \frac{M\,m}{M + m}\,v_0,$$

where v_0 is the velocity of the M-particle in the laboratory system. Because of the laws of conservation of energy and momentum the result of the collision in the centre of mass system is reduced to a rotation of the momenta of the two particles through an angle ϑ (Fig. 26). This angle depends upon the type of interaction.

To find the momenta of the particles after the collision in the laboratory system one must add OC and OC' vectorially to AO and OB respectively, the latter being equal to MV and mV, V is the velocity of the centre of mass

$$\mathbf{V} = \frac{m\,\mathbf{v_0}}{M + m}.$$

In this way we obtain the momenta AC and CB, whose relative position depends on the position of the point C on the circumference.

(b) When $M = m$, the point A (Fig. 26) lies on the circumference; for $M < m$ the point A is inside the circumference.

14.6. From Fig. 26 one can see at once that φ_{max} occurs when the vector AC (the momentum of the meson in the laboratory system after the collision) becomes a tangent to the circumference. Hence

$$\sin \varphi_{max} = \frac{OB}{AO} = \frac{m}{M}, \quad \varphi_{max} = 16 \cdot 7'.$$

Here M and m are the masses of the meson and the electron respectively.

14.7. (a) The total momentum transmitted by the meson to the electron is obtained from the expression (Fig. 63)

$$p = \int_{-\infty}^{+\infty} f_n \, dt = 2 \int_{\pi/2}^{0} \frac{e^2 \cos \vartheta}{r^2 \dfrac{d\vartheta}{dt}} \, d\vartheta.$$

Since from the conservation of momentum we have

$$r^2 \frac{d\vartheta}{dt} = \text{const} = -v\,\varrho,$$

we find

$$p = \frac{2e^2}{v\,\varrho}.$$

Now we have to express v, the velocity of the meson, relativistically as a function of its kinetic energy and thus we obtain

$$\varrho = \frac{2e^2\left(1 + \dfrac{M\,c^2}{E}\right)}{p\,c\sqrt{1 + 2\dfrac{M\,c^2}{E}}},$$

where M is the mass of the meson.

(b) $\varrho = 5\cdot9 \times 10^{-12}$ cm.

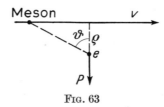

FIG. 63

14.8. The number of recoil electrons with energies within the range from E to $E + \mathrm{d}E$ is evidently

$$\mathrm{d}N = 2\pi\,\varrho\,\mathrm{d}\varrho\,n\,Z\,N,$$

where ϱ is the impact parameter of the meson corresponding to the recoil energy of the electron E, n the number of atoms in $1\,\mathrm{cm}^2$ of the cross-section of the beam, Z the number of electrons in each atom and N the intensity of the meson beam.

From the solution of the preceding problem we find a relation between the impact parameter ϱ of the meson and the kinetic energy of the recoil electron E:

$$\varrho^2 = \frac{2e^4}{m\,v^2\,E},$$

where m is the electron mass, and v the velocity of the meson. We substitute the result of differentiating this expression into the first equation and get:

$$\mathrm{d}N = \frac{2\pi\,n\,N\,Z\,e^4}{m\,v^2}\,\frac{\mathrm{d}E}{E^2}.$$

14.9. Into two γ-quanta: in "empty" space (outside the field of a nucleus). This follows from the law of conservation of momentum in the center of mass system. In the field of a nucleus a single gamma ray quantum can be emitted, the extra momentum being taken up by recoil of the nucleus.

14.10. (a) No.

(b) For the threshold value of the energy of the γ-quantum the relative velocity of the created particle and anti-particle is zero. In this case the laws of conservation of total energy and of momentum can be written as follows:

$$h\,\nu_{\mathrm{thr}} + M\,c^2 = \sqrt{(2\,m_0 + M)^2\,c^4 + p^2\,c^2},$$

$$\frac{h\,\nu_{\mathrm{thr}}}{c} = p,$$

where p is the total momentum of all the particles (including the recoil nucleus) after the creation of the pair. From these expressions we find

$$h\,\nu_{\mathrm{thr}} = \frac{(2\,m_0 + M)^2 - M^2}{2M} = 2\,m_0\,c^2\left(1 + \frac{m_0}{M}\right).$$

14.11.
$$\varDelta E = m_0\,c^2\,\frac{m_0}{M} = 0\cdot28\,\mathrm{keV},$$

where m_0 is the rest mass of the electron, M the mass of the nucleon.

14.12. From the condition $h\,\nu = 2\,\sqrt{p^2\,c^2 + m_0^2\,c^4}$, we have

$$\lambda = \frac{h\,c}{2\,\sqrt{e^2\,\varrho^2\,H^2 + m_0^2\,c^4}} = 1\cdot46 \times 10^{-8}\,\mathrm{\AA},$$

where ϱ is the radius of curvature, H the intensity of the magnetic field, and m_0 the rest mass of the electron.

14.13.
$$\tau_0 = \frac{\tau}{1 + \dfrac{E}{m_0\,c^2}} = 2\cdot2 \times 10^{-6}\,\mathrm{sec}.$$

14.14. From the law of conservation of energy we have

$$m_0\,c^2 = \sum_i \frac{m_{0\,i}\,c^2}{\sqrt{1 - \beta_i^2}},$$

where m_0 and m_{0i} are the rest masses of the decaying and the created particle. Hence it is evident that

$$m_0 > \sum_i m_{0i}.$$

The mass defect in this decay depends on the partial transformation of the rest energy of the particle m_0 into the kinetic energy of the created particle and the energy of the photons (if any).

14.15. 0·78 MeV.

14.16. $$\frac{E_\nu}{E_\mu} = 1 + 2\frac{m_\mu}{\Delta m} = 7·22,$$

where E_ν and E_μ are the energies of the neutrino and of the μ-meson, whose mass is m_μ and Δm is the mass defect corresponding to this decay.

14.17. $$v \approx c\sqrt{\frac{\Delta m(\Delta m + 2m\pi)}{m_n m_\Sigma}} = 6·1 \times 10^9 \text{ cm/sec},$$

where Δm is the mass defect of the decay and m_π, m_n and m_Σ are the rest masses of the π-meson, the neutron and the Σ^- particle respectively.

14.18. When the kinetic energy of the incoming particle is equal to the threshold value E_{thr}, the relative velocity of the created particles m' and M' is zero. Therefore the laws of conservation of the total energy and momentum can be written as follows:

$$E_{thr} + m c^2 + M c^2 = \sqrt{(m' + M')^2 c^4 + p^2 c^2}.$$

Here p is the total momentum of the $m' + M'$ system and is equal to the momentum of the incoming particle. It is related to E_{thr} by the expression

$$(m c^2 + E_{thr})^2 = m^2 c^4 + p^2 c^2.$$

Eliminating p from these two expression, we get

$$E_{thr} = \frac{(m' + M')^2 - (m + M)^2}{2M} c^2.$$

14.19. $$p + p \rightarrow \pi^+ + d,$$

d is a deuteron. 290 MeV.

14.20. $6\, m c^2$; 3·06 MeV $(e \rightarrow e)$; 5630 MeV $(p \rightarrow p)$.

14.21. 10·52 MeV.

14.22. From the laws of conservation of energy and momentum

$$E_K + Q = E_\pi,$$

$$p_K = p_\pi,$$

where Q is the reaction energy, we find that

$$E_K = \frac{\Delta m \, m_K}{2 m_\pi} c^2 = 407 \cdot 5 \text{ MeV.}$$

Here Δm is the mass defect of the reaction and m_K and m_π are the rest masses of K^0 and π^0-meson respectively.

14.23.
$$\cos\frac{\varphi}{2} = \sqrt{\frac{E(E + 2 m_K c)}{(Q + E_K)(Q + E_K + 4 m_\pi c^2)}}.$$

Hence $\varphi = 102 \cdot 5°$.

Here Q is the reaction energy and m_K and m_π the rest masses of K^0 and π^0-meson respectively.

14.24. $p_\Lambda = 149 \text{ MeV}/c$, where c is the velocity of light; 41°.

14.25. At an angle of 7·5° relative to the direction of motion of the xi-hyperon.

15.1.
$$n = \frac{\pi \, d^3 \, \varrho \, g \tan \alpha}{6 \, e \, E} = 5 \,.$$

15.2. (a)
$$q = \frac{9\pi \, \eta \, (v_1 + v_2)}{2 \, E} \sqrt{\frac{(v_2 - v_1) \, \eta}{g \, (\varrho - \varrho_0) \left(1 + A \dfrac{\lambda}{r}\right)^3}} \,.$$

(b)
$$\frac{\Delta q}{q} = 1 - \frac{1}{\left(1 + 2A \dfrac{\lambda}{d}\right)^{3/2}} = 21 \cdot 7 \% \,.$$

15.3. See Reference 1.

15.4.
$$m = \frac{e^2 \, H^2 \, l^4}{8 \, c^2 \, s^2 \, E} = 203$$

electron masses. Here H is the field intensity, l the length of the trajectory in the field, s the deflection, and c the velocity of light.

15.5.
$$H = \frac{2 \, c \, s}{l \, (l + 2L)} \sqrt{\frac{2m \, U}{e}} = 223 \text{ oe} \,.$$

15.6. (a)
$$\frac{e}{m} = \frac{2 \, f^2 \, L^2}{n^2 \, U} \,,$$

where $n = 1, 2, 3, \ldots$
(b) $4 \cdot 7 \times 10^7$ c/s.

15.7.
$$\varrho = \frac{m \, v \, c}{e \, H} \sim p \,.$$

Hence one easily obtains that for monoenergetic particles

$$\varrho \sim \sqrt{m} \,.$$

15.8. (a) $\Delta x = \dfrac{2c}{H} \sqrt{\dfrac{2U}{e \, N}} \, (\sqrt{M_1} - \sqrt{M_2}) = 0 \cdot 788$ cm.

Here N is Avogadro's number and M_1 and M_2 the isotope masses in mass units.

(b) $\Delta x/\Delta M = 0{\cdot}788$ cm/mass units.

15.9. U^{234} and U^{235} cannot be separated, U^{238} can be separated from the given mixture of isotopes.

15.10. $\dfrac{e}{m} = \dfrac{v\,c}{\varrho\,H} = 0{\cdot}96 \times 10^5$ coul/g.

15.11. $7{\cdot}8 \times 10^6$ particles/cm^2 sec.

15.12. During each second the counter cannot register for a time τn sec. During this time $\tau n n_0$ particles pass through it, but are not registered. Thus

$$\tau\, n\, n_0 = n_0 - n,$$

whence $n_0 = \dfrac{n}{1 - \tau\, n} = 556$ particles/sec.

The relative error is

$$\frac{\Delta n}{n_0} = \tau\, n = 10\%\,.$$

15.13. 10^4 pulses.

15.14. Neglecting the background, the relative error is

$$\frac{\sqrt{N_x}}{N_x}\,.$$

Taking the background into account, and since $N_\varphi = N_x$

$$\frac{\sqrt{N_{\varphi+x} + N_x}}{N_{\varphi+x} - N_x} = \sqrt{\frac{6}{N_{\varphi+x}}}\,.$$

Comparing these two results we have

$$N_{\varphi+x} = 6N_x\,.$$

15.15. $v = \sqrt{\dfrac{2d\,e\,E\,(2L - d)}{m\,(4L - d)}} = 3{\cdot}8 \times 10^9$ cm/sec,

where e and m are the charge and the mass of the proton.

15.17. (a) $\qquad E = E_0 + e\,E_x\,L \approx 10^3$ MeV.

(b) Integrating the equation of motion twice

$$\frac{\mathrm{d}}{\mathrm{d}t}\left(\frac{m\,v}{\sqrt{1 - \beta^2}}\right) = e\,E_x$$

and finding the integration constants from the initial conditions we get

$$v(x) = \frac{c \sqrt{(e\,E_x\,x + m_0\,c^2 + E_0)^2 - m_0^2\,c^4}}{e\,E_x\,x + m_0\,c^2 + E_0}.$$

15.18. (a)
$$T = \frac{2\pi\,m\,c}{e\,H},$$

i.e., it does not depend upon the energy of the particle. But this is true only when the kinetic energy of the particle is considerably smaller than the energy equivalent of its rest mass.

(b)

Particle	ϱ (cm)	(T sec)
electron	0·241	3·57 × 10^{-10}
proton	442·5	6·55 × 10^{-7}
alpha particle	878·0	1·31 × 10^{-6}

15.19.
$$E_{\max} = \frac{e^2\,\varrho^2\,H^2}{2\,m\,c^2}.$$

Respectively: 4·31; 2·16 and 4·35 MeV.

15.20.
$$f = \frac{1}{\pi\,\varrho}\sqrt{\frac{2\,E}{m}} = 9\;\text{Mcps}.$$

15.21. After determining the velocity of the alpha particle we find R from Geiger's expression (see the introduction to Chapter 12). Hence we find the range in aluminium L. Using the expression for L we find the equivalent thickness of the window from the expression given in the problem. Thus we obtain 12·4 cm.

15.22.
$$T = \frac{2\pi\,E}{c\,e\,H},$$

where E is the total energy of the particle.

Energy (MeV)	T for electrons (mμsec)	T protons (mμsec)
1	0·105	65·6
100	6·99	72·5
10,000	698	763

15.23. $h = 2\pi E/eH\lambda = 8$.

15.24. 16·6 per cent.

15.25. (a) 10^{10} particles/cm^2 sec,
(b) 10^{14} particles/cm^2 sec.

15.26.
$$E = \frac{e\,n}{c}\,\frac{\mathrm{d}\Phi}{\mathrm{d}t} = 20 \text{ MeV,}$$

where n is the number of revolutions, and $\dfrac{\mathrm{d}\Phi}{\mathrm{d}t}$ the rate of change of the magnetic flux through a surface inside the orbit.

15.27. 4 MeV; 0·0031 Å.

15.28. (a) On the equilibrium orbit

$$\frac{m\,v^2}{\varrho_0} = \frac{e}{c}\,v\,H(\varrho_0).$$

When ϱ deviates from ϱ_0 this equation is not valid, since the left and right hand sides of the expression depend differently on ϱ. An additional force $\varDelta f$ will arise:

$$\frac{m\,v^2}{\varrho} = \frac{e}{c}\,v\,H(\varrho) + \varDelta f.$$

From Fig. 64 it is evident that this additional force will tend to restore the particle into the equilibrium orbit, for any deviation of ϱ from ϱ_0.

(b) $\varDelta f = \dfrac{\eta(1-n)E}{\varrho_0}\,\dfrac{1 + 2\dfrac{m_0 c^2}{E}}{1 + \dfrac{m_0 c^2}{E}} = \begin{cases} 1\cdot18 \times 10^{-10}\,d(E = E_1) \\ 0\cdot67 \times 10^{-8}\,d(E = E_2) \end{cases}$

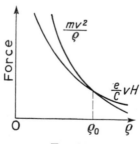

FIG. 64

15.29. 173 MeV.

15.30. The basic idea of the principle of self-focusing can be easily grasped from Fig. 65, which shows how the intensity of the electric field in the accelerating gaps depends on time.

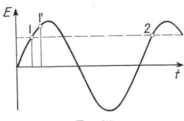

FIG. 65

A particle is said to be resonant when it covers the distance between two accelerating gaps in an interval of time equal to one half the period of oscillation of the accelerating field. Such a particle is in exact resonance with the variable electric field. It is indicated in Fig. 65 by points 1 and 2. A particle which is not in resonance however, one which, for example, lags somewhat, falls into the accelerating gap at a later instant when E is larger (point $1'$). Such a particle is accelerated more strongly and tends to catch up with the resonant particle. And conversely, a particle gaining a little relative to the resonant phase tends to stay back. An exact calculation show that these particles tend to stay about the resonant phase (resonant particles) undergoing only small oscillations about it.

It should be pointed out that only those particles which enter the accelerating gaps at instants when the field E is increasing are included in the self accelerating regime. One can easily show that all other particles are completely excluded from the accelerating process.

15.31. See Reference 3.

15.32. (a) $4 \cdot 55 \times 10^6$ revolutions, 910,000 km;

(b) $4 \cdot 47 \times 10^3$ oe/sec;

(c) $0 \cdot 9963\, c$, where c is the velocity of light.

15.33. $$E_{\text{rel}} = 2E\left(\frac{E}{E_0} + 2\right) = 1430 \text{ GeV},$$

where E is the rest energy of the proton ($m_0 c^2$).

Appendices

APPENDICES

1. Abbreviations

Unit	Abbreviation	Unit	Abbreviation
ampere	amp	gram (mass)	g
ångstrom (10^{-8} cm)	Å	henry	H
atmospheres	atm	hertz (cycles per second)	c/s
bar (10^6 d/cm^2)	bar	hour	hr
barn (10^{-21} cm^2)	b	joule	joule
calorie	cal	kilogram (mass)	kg
Calorie (10^3 calorie)	Cal	kilogram-metre	kg-m
centimetre	cm	kilogram-weight	kg-wt
coulomb	coul	litre	litre
curie	C	maxwell	maxwell
degrees Centigrade	°C	mass units	MU
degrees Kelvin (absolute)	°K	metre	m
		micron	μ
dyne	d	minute	min
electromagnetic units	emu	oersted	oe
		ohm	ohm, Ω
electrostatic units	esu	radian	rad
erg	erg	roentgen	r
farad	farad	second	sec
fermi (10^{-13} cm)	f	volt	V
gauss	gauss	watt	W

2. DECIMAL PREFIXES OF UNITS

Prefix	Ratio to the principal unit	Notation
mega	10^6	M
kilo	10^3	k
centi	10^2	c
mili	10^{-3}	m
micro	10^{-6}	μ

Examples: millimicron $m\mu$
million electron volt MeV
microfarad μf

3. WORK FUNCTION OF METALS

Metal	A, eV	Metal	A, eV
Aluminium	3·74	Molybdenum	4·27
Barium	2·29	Nickel	4·84
Caesium	1·89	Platinum	5·29
Calcium	2·76	Potassium	2·15
Copper	4·47	Rubidium	2·13
Gold	4·58	Silver	4·28
Iron	4·36	Sodium	2·27
Lithium	2·39	Tungsten	4·50
Magnesium	3·46	Uranium	3·74
Mercury	4·52	Zinc	3·74

4. Ionization Potentials of Atoms and Molecules

Element	U_i (in volts)	Element	U_i (in volts)
Argon	5·7	Mercury	10·4
Caesium	3·9	Neon	21·5
Calcium	6·0	Nitrogen N	14·5
Chlorine	13·0	N_2	15·8
Helium	24·5	Oxygen O	13·5
Hydrogen H	13·6	O_2	12·5
H_2	15·4	Potassium	4·3
Lithium	5·4	Rubidium	4·2
Krypton	14·0	Sodium	5·1
Magnesium	7·6	Xenon	12·1

5. Densities of Metals

Metal	g/cm³	Metal	g/cm³
Aluminium	2·7	Platinum	21·5
Bismuth	9·8	Plutonium	16·4−19·0
Cadmium	8·65	Potassium	0·86
Copper	8·9	Silver	10·5
Gold	19·3	Sodium	0·97
Iron	7·8	Thorium	11·5
Lead	11·3	Tin	7·4
Magnesium	1·74	Tungsten	19·1
Mercury	13·6	Uranium	18·7
Nickel	8·9	Zinc	7·0

6. Values of Definite Integrals

1. $\displaystyle\int_0^\infty \frac{x^n\,dx}{e^x-1} = \begin{cases} 1\cdot645 & (n=1), \\ 2\cdot405 & (n=2), \\ 6\cdot49 & (n=3), \\ 24\cdot9 & (n=4). \end{cases}$

2. $\displaystyle\int_0^\infty x^n e^{-x}\,dx = n!$ for positive integers n

3. $\displaystyle\int_0^\infty x^n e^{-x^2}\,dx = \begin{cases} \dfrac{\sqrt{\pi}}{2} & \text{for } n=0 \\[2mm] \dfrac{k!}{2} & \text{for odd integers } n\ (n=2k+1) \\[2mm] \dfrac{1\cdot3\cdots(2k-1)}{2^{k+1}}\sqrt{\pi} & \text{for even integers } n\ (n=2k) \end{cases}$

4. $\displaystyle\int_0^\infty e^{-x^2}\,dx \approx 0\cdot843.$

7. Constants of Diatomic Molecules

Molecule	Distance between nuclei d (Å)	Vibrational frequency (cm^{-1})	Dissociation energy (eV)
H_2	0·741	4395·2	4·478
N_2	1·094	2359·6	7·37
O_2	1·207	1580·36	5·084
F_2	1·282	1139·8	~1·6
P_2	1·894	780·43	5·033
S_2	1·889	725·68	~4·4
Cl_2	1·988	564·9	2·48
Br_2	2·283	323·2	1·971
I_2	2·666	214·57	1·542
HF	0·917	4138·52	5·8
HCl	1·275	2989·74	4·431
HBr	1·413	2649·67	3·75
HI	1·604	2309·5	3·06
CO	1·128	2170·21	~9·7
NO	1·15	1906	5·29
OH	0·971	3735	4·35

8. Excitation Potentials of K- and L-series

Z	Element	K-series		L-series	
		Edge of the absorption band	Excitation potential	Edge of the absorption band	Excitation potential
		Å	kV	Å	kV
13	Al	7·936	1·56	—	—
23	V	2·263	5·48	—	—
24	Cr	2·066	6·02	—	—
25	Mn	1·892	6·55	—	—
26	Fe	1·739	7·14	—	—
27	Co	1·604	7·73	—	—
28	Ni	1·484	8·35	—	—
29	Cu	1·377	9·00	11·28	1·1
30	Zn	1·281	9·68	—	—
42	Mo	0·6181	20·1	4·290	2·9
47	Ag	0·4845	25·6	3·247	3·8
50	Sn	0·4239	29·2	2·770	4·5
74	W	0·1782	69·6	1·024	12·1
78	Pt	0·1577	78·7	0·891	13·9
79	Au	0·1535	80·7	0·862	14·4
82	Pb	0·1405	88·3	0·781	15·9
92	U	0·1075	115·3	0·568	21·8

9. PROPERTIES OF CERTAIN ISOTOPES

Z	Isotope	Mass of the atom in MU	Occurrence in the natural mixture of isotopes %	Type of transmutation. Half-life T
	n	1·00898	—	β^- (12·8 min)
	p	1·00759	—	
1	H^1	1·00814	99·985	
	H^2	2·01474	0·0156	
	H^3	3·01700	—	β^- (12·5 yr)
2	He	3·01698	$1·3 \times 10^{-4}$	
	He^4	4·00387	99·9999	
3	Li^6	6·01702	7·3	
	Li^7	7·01822	92·7	
4	Be^7	7·01915	—	e_K (52·9 days)
	Be^8	8·00785	—	2α (<1 sec)
	Be^9	9·01504	100	
5	B^{10}	10·01611	18·8	
	B^{11}	11·01279	81·2	
6	C^{11}	11·01492	—	β^+ (20·4 min)
	C^{12}	12·00380	98·9	
	C^{13}	13·00747	1·1	
7	N^{13}	13·00986	—	β^+ (9·9 min)
	N^{14}	14·00752	99·62	
	N^{15}	15·00486	0·38	
8	O^{15}	15·00777	—	β^+ (118 sec)
	O^{16}	16·00000	99·758	
	O^{17}	17·00453	0·039	
	O^{18}	18·00487	0·203	

Continued

Z	Isotope	Mass of the atom in MU	Occurrence in the natural mixture of isotopes %	Type of transmutation. Half-life T
9	F^{19}	19·00446	100	
10	Ne^{20}	19·99886	90·51	
	Ne^{21}	21·00059	0·28	
	Ne^{22}	21·99827	9·21	
11	Na^{23}	22,99714	100	
	Na^{24}	23·99865	–	β^- (15 hr)
12	Mg^{27}	26·99295	–	β^- (10 min)
13	Al^{27}	26·99014	100	
	Al^{28}	27·99083	–	β^- (2·3 min)
14	Si^{29}	28·98572	4·7	
15	P^{29}	28·98962	–	β^+ (4·6 sec)
	P^{30}	29·98817	–	β^+ (2·5 min)
	P^{31}	30·98362	100	
	P^{32}	31·98409	–	β^- (14·3 days)
16	S^{32}	31·98224	95·06	
	S^{33}	32·98213	0·74	
	S^{34}	33·97875	4·18	
	S^{35}	34·98022	–	β^- (87·1 days)
17	Cl^{37}	36·97762	24·57	
18	Ar^{36}	35·97893	0·307	
	Ar^{37}	36·97850	–	e_K (92%) (34·1 days)
19	K^{39}	38·9761	93·1	e_L (8%)
	K^{40}	39·9755	0·011	β^-, e_K ($1·3 \times 10^9$ yr)
	K^{41}	40·9749	6·9	
20	Ca^{40}	39·97542	96·9	

Continued

Z	Isotope	Mass of the atom in MU	Occurrence in the natural mixture of isotopes %	Type of transmutation. Half-life T
24	Cr^{52}	51·95693	83·8	
29	Cu^{63}	62·94862	69	
	Cu^{64}	63·94913	—	β^- (12·9 hr)
	Cu^{65}	64·94749	31	
47	Ag^{107}	106·9386	51·9	
	Ag^{108}	107·9401	—	β^- (2·3 min)
	Ag^{109}	108·940	48·1	
	Ag^{110}	109·94218	—	β^- (24·5 sec)
48	Cd^{113}	112·94206	12·26	
52	Te^{128}	127·94710	31·7	
43	J^{127}	126·94600	100	
	J^{128}	127·9466	—	β^- (27 min)
79	Au^{197}		100	
	Au^{198}		—	β^- (2·69 days)
82	Pb^{206}	206·03859	23·6	
	Pb^{207}	207·04090	22·6	
	Pb^{208}	208·04160	52·3	
	Pb^{210} (RaD)	210·04958	—	β^- (22·1 yr)
	Pb^{214} (RaB)	214·06633	—	β^- (26·8 min)
83	Bi^{210} (RaE)	210·04951	—	β^- (5 hr)
84	Po^{210} (RaF)	210·04826	—	α (138 days)
	Po^{212} (ThC′)	212·05487	—	α (3×10^{-7} sec)
	Po^{218} (RaA)	218·07676	—	α (99·96%) (3 min)
				β^- (0·04%)
86	Rn^{222} (Em)	222·08663	—	α (3·82 days)
88	Ra^{226}	226·09574	—	α (1622 yr)

Z	Isotope	Mass of the atom in MU	Occurrence in the natural mixture of isotopes %	Type of transmutation. Half-life T
92	U^{234}	234·11379	0·0055	α ($2\cdot67\times10^5$ yr)
	U^{235}	235·11704	0·714	α ($7\cdot07\times10^8$ yr)
	U^{236}	236·11912	—	
	U^{238}	238·12493	99·28	α ($4\cdot5\times10^9$ yr)
	U^{239}	239·12853	—	β^- (23·5 min)
94	Pu^{238}	238·12376	—	α (89·6 yr)
	Pu^{239}	239·12653	—	α ($2\cdot4\times10^4$ yr)

Note: e_K, e_L denotes K- and L-electron capture.

10. RADIOACTIVE SERIES OF URANIUM

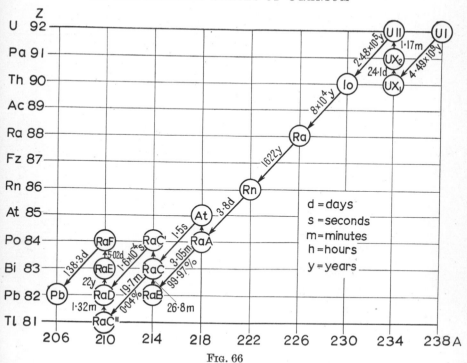

FIG. 66

11. ELEMENTARY PARTICLES

Class	Name	Symbol	Mass (in electron masses)	Spin	Nuclear charge	Isotopic spin I	Isotopic spin I_z	Strangeness	Lifetime	Decay scheme
	photon	γ	0	1	0	0			∞	
leptons	neutrino	ν	0	1/2	0				∞	
	anti-neutrino	$\tilde{\nu}$	0	1/2	0				∞	
	electron	e^-	1	1/2	0				∞	
	positron	e^+	1	1/2	0				∞	
	mu-mesons	μ^+	206.7	1/2	0				22.2×10^{-6}	$e^+ + \nu + \tilde{\nu}$
		μ^-	206.7	1/2	0				22.2×10^{-6}	$e^- + \nu + \tilde{\nu}$
mesons	pi-mesons	π^+	273.2	0	0	1	+1	0	2.56×10^{-8}	$\mu^+ + \nu$
		π^-	273.2	0	0	1	−1	0	2.56×10^{-8}	$\mu^- + \tilde{\nu}$
		π^0	264.2	0	0	1	0	0	$<4\times10^{-13}$	$\gamma+\gamma,\ \gamma+e^+ +e^-$
	K-mesons	K^+	966.5	0	0	1/2	+1/2	+1	1.22×10^{-8}	$\mu\pm+\nu,\ \mu\pm+\nu+\pi^0,\ e\pm+\nu+\pi^0,$
		K^-	966.5	0	0	1/2	−1/2	−1	1.22×10^{-8}	$\pi\pm+\pi^0,\ \pi\pm+\pi^+ +\pi^-,\ \pi\pm+2\pi^0$
		K^0	965	0	0	1/2	−1/2	+1	$K_1^0\,9.5\times10^{-11}$	$\pi^+ +\pi^-,\ 2\pi^0$
		$\tilde{K}^0$	965	0	0	1/2	+1/2	−1	$K_2^0\,3\times10^{-8}{-}10^{-6}$	$\pi\pm+e\mp+\nu,\ \pi\pm+\mu\mp+\nu,\ \pi^+ + \pi^- +\pi^0$
nucleons and anti-nucleons	proton	p	1836.1	1/2	+1	1/2	+1/2	0	∞	
	antiproton	$\tilde{\mathrm{p}}$	1836.1	1/2	−1	1/2	−1/2	0	∞	
	neutron	n	1838.6	1/2	+1	1/2	−1/2	0	1040	$\mathrm{p}+e^- +\tilde{\nu}$
	antineutron	$\tilde{\mathrm{n}}$	1838.6	1/2	−1	1/2	+1/2	0	1040	$\tilde{\mathrm{p}}+e^+ +\nu$
hyperons	lambda-particle	Λ^0	2182	1/2	+1	0	0	−1	2.77×10^{-10}	$\mathrm{p}+\pi^-,\ \mathrm{n}+\pi^0$
	sygma-particles	Σ^+	2325	1/2	+1	1	+1	−1	7.8×10^{-11}	$\mathrm{p}+\pi^0,\ \mathrm{n}+\pi^+$
		Σ^-	2341	1/2	+1	1	−1	−1	1.7×10^{-10}	$\mathrm{n}+\pi^-$
		Σ^0	2324	1/2	+1	1	0	−1	$<10^{-11}$	$\Lambda^0+\gamma$
	cascade	Ξ^-	2585	1/2	+1	1/2	−1/2	−2	$4.6\times10^{-10}{-}2\times10^{-8}$	$\Lambda^0+\pi^-$
	xi-hyperons	Ξ^0	?	1/2	+1	1/2	+1/2	−2	?	?

Note: The corresponding anti-hyperos are: $\tilde{\Lambda}^0$, $\tilde{\Sigma}^+$, $\tilde{\Sigma}^-$, $\tilde{\Sigma}^0$, $\tilde{\Xi}^-$ and $\tilde{\Xi}^0$.

12. RELATIONS BETWEEN ENERGY UNITS

Unit	eV	MU	Erg	Joule
1 eV	1	$1 \cdot 075 \times 10^{-9}$	$1 \cdot 6 \times 10^{-12}$	$1 \cdot 6 \times 10^{-19}$
1 MU	$9 \cdot 31 \times 10^{8}$	1	$1 \cdot 49 \times 10^{-3}$	$1 \cdot 49 \times 10^{-10}$
1 erg	$6 \cdot 25 \times 10^{11}$	$6 \cdot 71 \times 10^{2}$	1	10^{-7}
1 joule	$6 \cdot 25 \times 10^{18}$	$6 \cdot 71 \times 10^{9}$	10^{7}	1
1 cal	$2 \cdot 61 \times 10^{19}$	$2 \cdot 81 \times 10^{10}$	$4 \cdot 18 \times 10^{7}$	$4 \cdot 18$
1 kg-m	$6 \cdot 13 \times 10^{19}$	$6 \cdot 59 \times 10^{10}$	$9 \cdot 81 \times 10^{7}$	$9 \cdot 81$
1 litre-atm	$6 \cdot 33 \times 10^{20}$	$6 \cdot 81 \times 10^{11}$	$1 \cdot 013 \times 10^{9}$	$101 \cdot 3$

Unit	Cal	kg-m	Litre-atm
1 eV	$3 \cdot 83 \times 10^{-20}$	$1 \cdot 63 \times 10^{-20}$	$1 \cdot 58 \times 10^{-21}$
1 MU	$3 \cdot 56 \times 10^{-11}$	$1 \cdot 52 \times 10^{-11}$	$1 \cdot 47 \times 10^{-12}$
1 erg	$2 \cdot 39 \times 10^{-8}$	$1 \cdot 02 \times 10^{-8}$	$9 \cdot 87 \times 10^{-10}$
1 joule	$0 \cdot 239$	$0 \cdot 102$	$9 \cdot 87 \times 10^{-3}$
1 cal	1	$0 \cdot 427$	$4 \cdot 13 \times 10^{-2}$
1 kg-m	$2 \cdot 34$	1	$9 \cdot 68 \times 10^{-2}$
1 litre-atm	$24 \cdot 2$	$10 \cdot 3$	1

13. IMPORTANT ATOMIC AND NUCLEAR PHYSICS CONSTANTS

Velocity of light $c = 2 \cdot 99793 \times 10^{10}$ cm/sec

Gravitational constant $N = 6 \cdot 670 \times 10^{-8}$ cm^3/g . sec^2

Avogadro's number $N = 6 \cdot 024 \times 10^{23}$ mole^{-1}

Gas constant $R = 8 \cdot 314 \times 10^{7}$ erg/deg . mole

$= 1 \cdot 987$ cal/deg . mole

$= 0 \cdot 082$ litre-atm/deg . mole

Standard volume of a perfect gas $V_0 = 22 \cdot 42$ litre/mole

Boltzmann's constant $k = 1 \cdot 380 \times 10^{-16}$ erg/deg

Planck's constant $h = 6 \cdot 625 \times 10^{-27}$ erg . sec

$\hbar = h/2\pi = 1 \cdot 054 \times 10^{-27}$ erg . sec

Electronic charge $e = 4 \cdot 803 \times 10^{-10}$ esu

$= 1 \cdot 602 \times 10^{-20}$ emu

e/m for the electron $= 5 \cdot 273 \times 10^{17}$ esu/g

Faraday's number $F = Ne = 2 \cdot 894 \times 10^{14}$ esu/g . equiv.

$= 96,520$ k/g.equiv.

Stefan–Boltzmann constant

$$\sigma = \frac{\pi^2}{60} \frac{k^4}{\hbar^3 c^2}$$

$$= 5{\cdot}669 \times 10^{-5} \, \text{erg/cm}^2 \, \text{sec} \cdot \text{deg}^4$$

Wien's displacement law constant

$$b = \lambda_{\max} T = 0{\cdot}2898 \, \text{cm} \cdot \text{deg}$$

Rydberg's constant

for infinite mass

$$R_\infty = \frac{m \, e^4}{4 \pi \, \hbar^3 c} = 109{,}737{\cdot}31 \, \text{cm}^{-1}$$

for deuteron

$$R_D = 109{,}707{\cdot}42 \, \text{cm}^{-1}$$

for the hydrogen atom

$$R_H = 109{,}677{\cdot}58 \, \text{cm}^{-1}$$

First Bohr radius

$$\frac{\hbar^2}{m \, e^2} = 0{\cdot}529 \times 10^{-8} \, \text{cm}$$

Compton wavelength of the electron

$$\frac{h}{m \, c} = 0{\cdot}02426 \times 10^{-8} \, \text{cm}$$

$$\frac{h}{m_p \, c} = 1{\cdot}321 \times 10^{-13} \, \text{cm}$$

Classical radius of the electron

$$r_e = \frac{e^2}{m \, c^2}$$

$$= 2{\cdot}818 \times 10^{-13} \, \text{cm}$$

Fine structure constant

$$\alpha = \frac{e^2}{h \, c} = \frac{1}{137{\cdot}038}$$

Bohr magneton

$$\mu_0 = \frac{e \, h}{2 \, m \, c} = 0{\cdot}9273 \times 10^{-20} \, \text{erg/gauss}$$

Magnetic moment of the electron μ_e $1{\cdot}001145 \, \mu_0$

Nuclear magneton

$$\mu_\nu = \frac{e \, h}{2 m_{P_c}} = 5{\cdot}05 \times 10^{-24} \, \text{erg/gauss}$$

Magnetic moment (the maximum projection of μ_H)

of the proton $\mu_p = 2{\cdot}7928 \, \mu_{\text{nu}}$

of the neutron $\mu_n = -1{\cdot}9130 \, \mu_{\text{nu}}$

of the deuteron $\mu_D = 0{\cdot}8574 \, \mu_{\text{nu}}$

Gyromagnetic ratio

of the electron $g_e = 2$

of the proton $g_p = 5{\cdot}58$

of the neutron $g_n = -3{\cdot}82$

Mass unit (atomic unit of mass)

$$1 \text{ MU} = 1 \cdot 660 \times 10^{-24} \text{ g}$$
$$= 931 \cdot 16 \text{ MeV}$$

Mass (and energy equivalent)
   of the electron $m_e = 5 \cdot 488 \times 10^{-4} \text{ MU}$
$$= 9 \cdot 108 \times 10^{-28} \text{ g}$$
$$= 0 \cdot 511 \text{ MeV}$$
   of the proton $m_p = 1 \cdot 00759 \text{ MU}$
$$= 1 \cdot 6724 \times 10^{-24} \text{ g}$$
$$= 938 \cdot 23 \text{ MeV}$$
   of the neutron $m_n = 1 \cdot 00898 \text{ MU}$
$$= 1 \cdot 6748 \times 10^{-24} \text{ g}$$
$$= 939 \cdot 53 \text{ MeV}$$
   of the alpha particle $m_\alpha = 4 \cdot 00167 \text{ MU}$
$$= 6 \cdot 6444 \times 10^{-24} \text{ g}$$

Ratio of the proton and the
   electron masses $\dfrac{m_p}{m_e} = 1836 \cdot 13$
Ratio of the mass units of the
   chemical and physical scales

$$16 \cdot 00435 : 16 = 1 \cdot 00027$$

Velocity of 1 eV electron $v = 5 \cdot 94 \times 10^7 \text{ cm/sec}$
Temperature corresponding
   to 1 eV $T = 7730°\text{K} \ (1 \text{ eV} = 3/2 \ kT)$

1 curie corresponds to $3 \cdot 7 \times 10^{10}$ decays per sec

1 roentgen corresponds to the quantity of X- or γ-rays which, in 1 cm^3 of dry air at NTP, forms 1 esu of electric charge of either sign, i.e. $2 \cdot 08 \times 10^9$ ion pairs.